Y0-CMK-404

The Illustrated Library of
NATURE

VOLUME 2

ANIMAL TRAITS—(cont.)

ANIMAL WORLD

The American Museum of Natural History

Cooperated in the publication of this edition.

The opinions expressed by authors are their own and do not necessarily reflect the policy of the Museum.

The Illustrated Library of
NATURE

THIS PICTORIAL ENCYCLOPEDIA of natural history and ecology depicts the relationships of all living organisms to each other and between them and their environments. Original manuscript from the *Doubleday Nature Programs* plus new articles and illustrations are included in this edition.

H. S. STUTTMAN CO., INC., Publishers
New York, N. Y., 10016

COPYRIGHT © 1971 BY

H. S. STUTTMAN CO., INC.

Copyright © 1952, 1953, 1954, 1955, 1956, 1957, 1958, 1959, 1960, 1961, 1962, 1963, 1965, 1966, 1967, 1968, 1969, by Nelson Doubleday, Inc.

Library of Congress Catalogue Card Number: 79-158363

Printed in the United States of America
All Rights Reserved

Contents

VOLUME 2

ANIMAL TRAITS—(cont.)

WEAPONS 134
▶ *The devices that nature gives the animals to protect themselves and hunt their food.*

ANIMAL WORLD

INVENTIONS IN NATURE 168
▶ *Techniques and tools developed and employed by man but originating in natural abilities possessed by animals.*

NATURE IN MOTION 202
▶ *The many ways in which mammals, birds, fish and even simpler animals move about on land, in the water and in the air.*

TRACKS AND TRAILS 240
▶ *What you can tell about animals from the clues and footprints they leave behind.*

▶ *The devices that nature gives the animals to protect themselves and hunt their food.*

Weapons

WHEN WE SPEAK OF ANIMALS as using weapons we are to some extent being influenced in our thinking by what we know of human motivation. The truth is that remarkably few animals have special weapons, either offensive or defensive. Most animals do what primitive man used to do before ever he learned to chip stones or fashion implements of any kind. To a large extent they avoid fighting. It is man's weapons that have made him aggressive.

The lion, for example, the king of beasts, and one therefore that should by human thinking possess many weapons with which to defend his kingdom, has only his teeth and his claws. Basically both have as their primary purpose the catching, killing and eating of food, and a lion uses them for this purpose all his life. Indeed, a lion could very well go through his whole lifetime with never a fight. Even if he does fight, he merely uses to defend himself the tools intended to kill prey. Far more often he uses bluff to survive, as do the majority of animals.

A particularly illuminating example of the use of bluff is to be found in the actions of the non-venomous European grass snake. Its usual food consists of frogs, newts and fishes, which it seizes with its teeth and swallows. When disturbed, the grass snake's first reaction is to slither into long grass or undergrowth, to get out of sight; and unless it is lethargic, because the day is cool, it will do this with

In general, very few animals have special **weapons** other than those that are essential for their survival. Even the most impressive set of **teeth**—large canines or long, pointed fangs—are primarily used in food-getting tactics. In the photograph above (top right) a yawning Everglades **alligator** exhibits its powerful jaws.

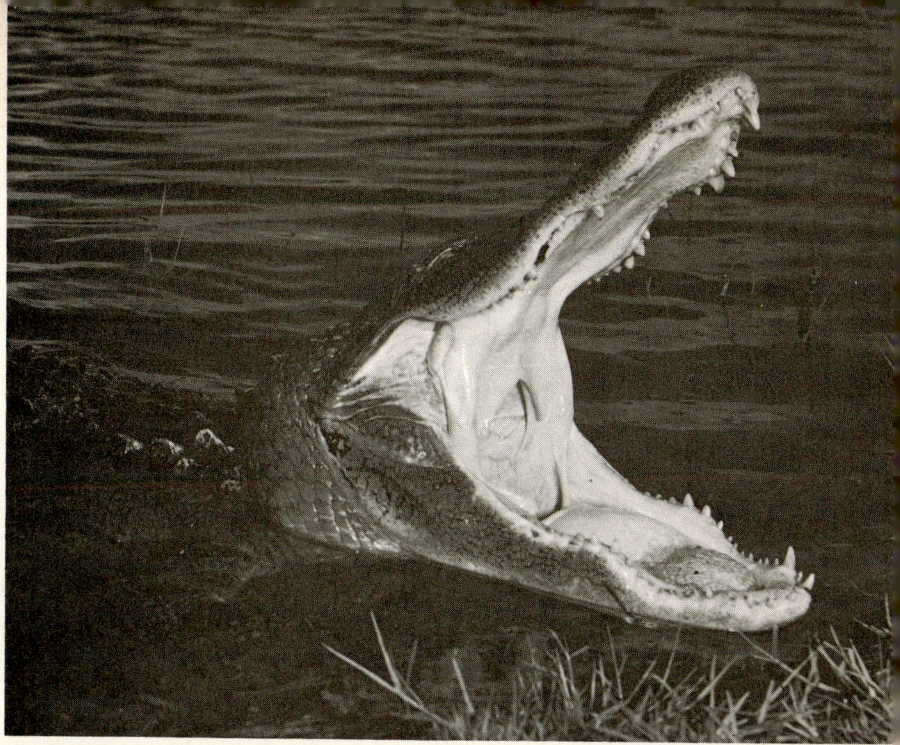

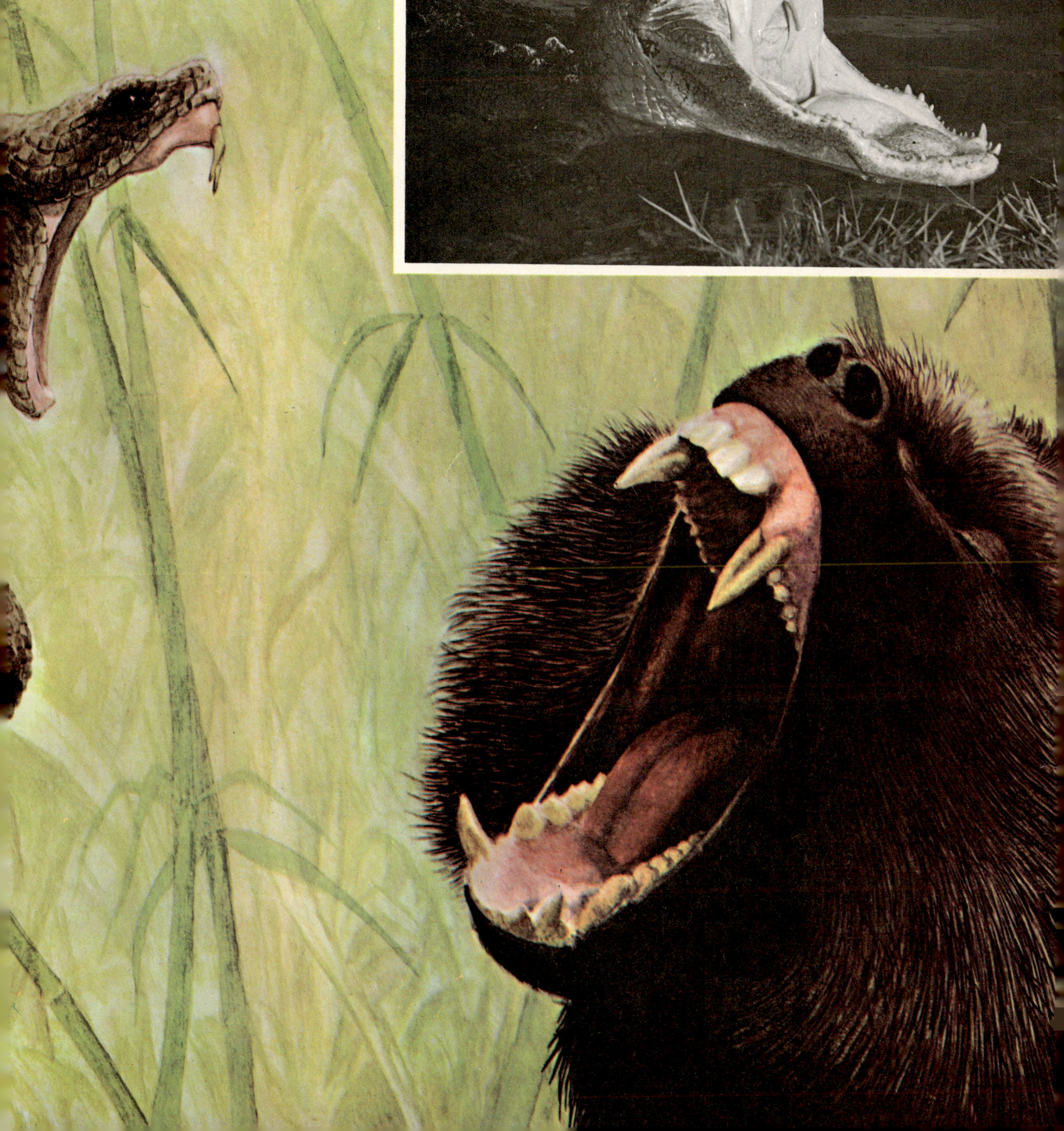

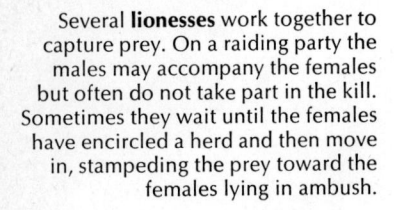

Several **lionesses** work together to capture prey. On a raiding party the males may accompany the females but often do not take part in the kill. Sometimes they wait until the females have encircled a herd and then move in, stampeding the prey toward the females lying in ambush.

surprising speed. When it cannot escape it may do one of several things, or it may do each in turn. It may strike at your hand, if you stoop to pick it up, hitting your hand with its teeth. This is quite ineffective when dealing with a human being, although it might cause a smaller enemy to hesitate or draw back momentarily, but only momentarily. The next action by the grass snake may be to give out a noxious secretion from the region of the vent. This is fairly unbearable to the human nostrils, but we have little information about how far it would deter an animal attacking the snake. The third action is to "sham dead". In this case the snake flops over on its back. Its body goes limp. Its mouth opens and the tongue lolls out. To all appearances the snake is dead; and if you turn it over on its front it will immediately twist over on its back and again its body will go limp, the mouth will gape and the tongue will loll out. The hog-nosed snake of the United States does the same thing.

Except for striking with the teeth, there is nothing in this series of actions to suggest any special weapons, and even the use of the teeth is more bluff than effective attack. The other two can, at most, be called passively defensive. In using these tactics, the grass snake epitomizes the activity of the majority of animals, which is first to seek escape, then to try bluffing. Even the obnoxious scent is of little value against enemies such as birds, which have a poor sense of smell.

Among animals most of what we call fighting starts and ends as mere bluff. They snarl, hiss, bare their teeth or open their beaks, as the case may be, make themselves look larger than life by blowing themselves out or by raising their feathers or fur, and generally try to intimidate their enemies or opponents. Probably in far less than one per cent of instances does any serious fighting result. Furthermore, although there are spectacular photographs of fights to the death between two animals, these are very few indeed, and the likelihood is, were it possible to reduce this to percentages, we should find that the number of animals which die fighting would be found to be a very small fraction of one per cent of the total population of animals.

Teeth and Claws as Weapons

Unless we have studied the subject we are apt to be influenced in our thinking about wildlife by what we experience with animals familiar to us in everyday life, and especially by the actions of dogs. These are a special case, however, since the breeds of domestic dog have to a large extent been selected for use as watchdogs and protectors. They are also living under artificial conditions, so that their way of behaving tends to depart from the natural. Nevertheless, the domestic dog furnishes a good example of how teeth are used as weapons. Anyone bitten by a dog will find on examining the wound that the dog's canine teeth have been the chief cause of the injury. These may be used either to give a straightforward bite or, more usually, to give a slashing cut. These methods are precisely the ones used by wild members of the dog family in attacking living prey. So they are primarily food-getting tactics adapted for offensive or defensive attack.

Flesh eaters such as cats, which have retractile claws that are not blunted by contact with the ground, use the claws as well as the canine teeth in fighting. When we handle such animals and they

(left)
Reaching high for a piece of fruit, the **elephant** uses its **trunk,** an organ specially adapted for such purposes. The trunk is never used as a weapon. In fact, when charging, the elephant protects its trunk by keeping it coiled up behind its tusks, where it won't be harmed.

(below)
Dusk is the usual hunting time for the **lion,** because the antelope's keen eyesight make it a more difficult prey to stalk during the day. The king of beasts has only his teeth and claws for weapons, and these are used mainly for the catching, killing and eating of food. Indeed, the lion never kills except to eat.

138 / ANIMAL TRAITS

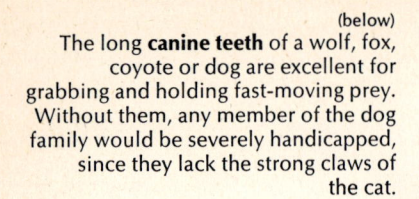

(below)
The long **canine teeth** of a wolf, fox, coyote or dog are excellent for grabbing and holding fast-moving prey. Without them, any member of the dog family would be severely handicapped, since they lack the strong claws of the cat.

(above)
While most **bears** will eat almost anything, their reputation as man-eaters is undeserved. Generally they flee to the woods as soon as man comes into view. Despite their great strength and powerful claws, they are usually mild animals, feeding on small mammals, fish, insects, fruit, vegetables and—when available—honey.

Although a **brown bear** (below, left) can kill a deer or an ox with one blow and rip up its enemies with its claws, it more frequently uses its paws to paddle fish into biting range and its claws for digging up roots or opening up a bees' nest. A more ferocious hunter is the **leopard** (below, right), which combines powerful claws with sharp teeth, great strength and incredible speed. Smaller than the lion or tiger, it can readily hide and ambush its victims.

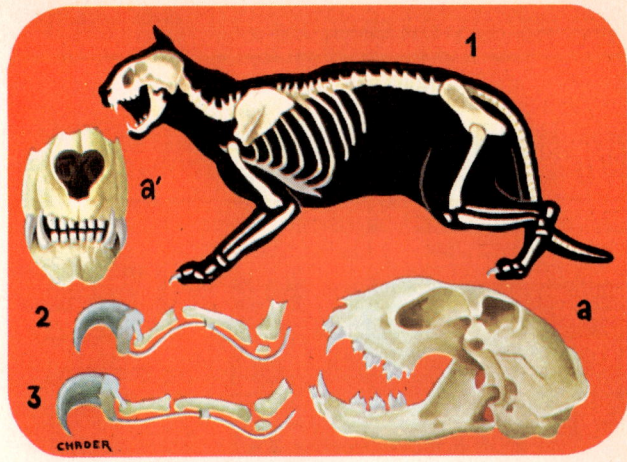

attack us the injuries show up for what they are: scratches, or deep but small wounds from the canine teeth, which, in the smaller carnivores, are needle-sharp. In cats of any description the claws and the teeth are primarily for holding and killing prey.

Bears use the front paws in a swiping blow, the long powerful claws inflicting deep scratches. It is the same use of the paw that comes into action when a bear kills large game, such as a deer, felling it with one blow, usually breaking the neck or back; and a similar movement with the paw is used to flip fish out of the river, while the claws are used mainly for digging up roots and tubers or opening up a bees' nest.

A sloth will defend itself with a swinging blow from the long front legs, the paws of which are armed with long hooklike claws. These claws also have a quite different primary function, that of hanging from branches.

In general, therefore, teeth and claws, even though they may be used as weapons, cannot be considered as special weapons except in a few animals. Teeth may be considered as special weapons in a few mammals, and claws mainly in birds of prey. Among mammals pigs have tusks which can inflict grievous wounds when used with a swinging blow of the head. The hippopotamus, related to pigs, also has long tusks that can be of little use in food-getting, but are formidable in a fight. Peccaries, the South American equivalent of the Old World pigs, use their teeth offensively. White-lipped peccaries especially will, when brought to bay, stand their ground in herds of up to 200, in close formation, champing their tusks, which are found in the lower jaw only, and making determined charges. White-lipped peccaries are said to use these same offensive tactics if one of their number is attacked, the whole herd combining to defend it.

Some deer have only tiny horns, and the chevrotains or mouse-deer have none at all. The mouse-deer have tusklike canines in the upper

(above, left)
The **wildcat** is an excellent climber and can leap from branch to branch, surprising prey, including birds in their nests. On the ground it generally hunts small game and rodents, each animal hunting alone and marking off a territory by leaving claw marks on a tree. Although it resembles a domestic cat in appearance, it has a reputation for untamable ferocity.

(above, right)
A **cat's skeleton** (1) provides a clear picture of how well-equipped these flesh eaters are to hunt and kill their prey. The **claws,** which may be drawn in (2) or extended (3), are not blunted by contact with the ground; and the **teeth** (a and a') are strong and sharp. Both claws and teeth are used for killing and holding the prey.

140 / ANIMAL TRAITS

(below)
In packs, **African hunting dogs** can bring down even the swiftest antelope by relay-running, killing it with slashing bites of their powerful teeth. They are built for speed, and their claws, which cannot be retracted, allow them greater traction in running. Because they kill more than they actually need for food, they are considered very savage animals.

(below, left)
A hornless deer, the **chevrotain,** or **mouse deer,** is timid and tends to flee when pursued, usually into the waters of the swampy areas it inhabits. It is not totally unarmed, however, for the male has canine teeth sharp enough to be effective weapons.

(below, right)
The **hippopotamus** lives in family groups in East Africa, feeding on water plants and roaming short distances at night to browse on shrubbery. In general it will head for the brush or water when surprised, but when confronted it has formidable **tusks,** which, although of little value in food-gathering, are quite useful for defense.

jaw, and the musk deer and the muntjacs, whose males have only very small antlers, have similar tusklike canines in addition to the antlers. All these animals use the canines with a swinging blow of the head as offensive weapons.

Aspects of Animal Combat

THE HUMAN RACE has produced such a variety of weapons that it has long been weapon-conscious. We have put these weapons to such continual use that we find it difficult to believe that constant warfare, or the ever-present threat of fighting, is more a human habit than one which governs the lives of animals. It is imperative therefore in discussing animal weapons to be clear about the kind of combat in which they might be employed.

The defensive weapon should, as a first principle, be used to ensure survival in the presence of a predator. Yet the fact is that most animals seem not to defend themselves from a predator. There are exceptions, and one of these is the mother with young; yet in the majority of instances in which teeth or claws, or even horns or antlers, are the only weapons possessed by a species, the female possesses them in a less well-developed form or lacks them entirely.

The situation that exists between the stoat or weasel, a predator, and the rabbit, its prey, will illustrate this observation. A stoat will pursue a rabbit by following its scent trail. When finally the stoat catches up with it the rabbit squeals and remains immobile, apparently unable to move, and submits to the *coup de grâce* with no attempt to defend itself. On the other hand, many a person in picking up a wild rabbit has sustained long and deep scratches in his forearm as the rabbit lashed out with its hind legs. To show the mighty potential for aggression in the hind legs of a rabbit we can quote the account, which probably is not isolated, of a doe rabbit with young that lashed out at

(above)
In both offensive and defensive tactics, the **saw-whet owl** is well prepared. When attacked, it falls on its back and presents its **talons** to the enemy. In its nighttime search for prey—usually mice—the owl is assisted by excellent vision, powerful talons and a **hooked beak** surrounded by sensory bristles through which it "feels" its prey.

(right)
The sharp, curved **talons** of the eagle will pierce the toughest animal hide easily, enabling it to kill quickly. They also afford a strong grip, so that the eagle can fly away with its prey without fear of dropping it.

142 / ANIMAL TRAITS

a stoat that came near her babies, kicking it sixteen feet through the air.

There are many similar examples, and from these we could make the deduction that if the prey species used such weapons as they possess, and used them always as they show they can by the exceptional cases, the carnivores would soon go hungry.

The next aspect of fighting can be best expressed by the popular phrase, used so frequently and uncritically by writers on the subject, about two males fighting for a female. All the evidence that has accumulated during the course of the last decade suggests that if males ever fight over a female the event must be a very rare one. What they do fight over is territory, and since a female is usually present in the territory, and is, as often as not, standing near the two male protagonists, there is the appearance, and no more, of the males fighting for possession of her.

In territorial fighting, which is the main cause of active combat, much of the aggressive display is threat or bluff. Actual fights are very few. Those that result in injury are even fewer, and those that result in actual death are very rare indeed.

To sum up, bloody combat, warfare and specific weapons are the exception rather than the rule among animals.

If we exclude teeth and claws as special weapons, it is less easy to do the same with antlers and horns. Yet even here there is room for doubt. The first of these, the antlers, are possessed only by deer, and in most species of deer only the males have antlers. They are, in fact, what are known as secondary sexual characteristics, as is the beard in the male human. When two male deer indulge in a fight in the breeding season it is primarily a fight over territory, and for the possession of the females only secondarily. Moreover, duels between male deer are more a matter of a clash of foreheads. The two protagonists may spar with their antlers, but this is a preliminary to a tremendous butting with the forehead. There are instances on record of one protagonist

(below, left)
Wolves, hawks and owls prey on the **rabbit**, despite its natural camouflage. A mother rabbit has some defense, however; her back legs can sometimes **kick** an intruder away. Yet the rabbit's main method of survival is probably overpopulation, often posing a problem to farmers and gardeners.

(below, right)
Underpopulation is the problem with the **bighorn**, because of hunting and the spread of civilization. Fantastic jumpers, they can make 20-foot leaps at breakneck speed, hopping from one precipice to another. When fighting for females, the bighorns charge head-on, and sometimes the very force of the blow is enough to kill one of the opponents.

(left)
Although **elephants** have powerful **tusks** for fighting, they will sometimes play at fighting between themselves, using their tusks so gently that they never hurt each other. Tusks are really well-developed teeth. The largest one known is close to eleven feet long and weighs over 200 pounds.

(left)
The enormous, palmlike **antlers** of the male **American elk** are useful in settling many disputes, often over a female. Well equipped for combat, bulls measure up to five feet in height and may weigh 1,000 pounds. Antlers may be several feet long and are completely regrown each year.

(below)
While a **chameleon's tongue** is not strictly a weapon, it can be flashed out and back boomerang fashion, sweeping in a passing fly. The tongue is club-shaped and sticky at the end. When shot out it can extend farther than the length of the head and the body, and it almost always strikes its mark.

sustaining injury from one of the tines of an opponent's antlers, but it must remain a matter of opinion how far there is deliberate and purposeful use of the antlers as actual weapons. It is more significant that in at least two species, the European elk and its counterpart, the North American moose, the males present their antlers to each other in sexual, or territorial, battles, but that they strike with their front hoofs at a predator. We could liken their antlers to duelling weapons, and their hoofs to real defensive weapons.

The horns worn by the members of the family *Bovidae*, which includes cattle, sheep, goats and antelopes, have a greater claim to be called weapons in the strict sense. There is, for example, the recorded instance of a herd of African buffalo which killed a lion. One of the

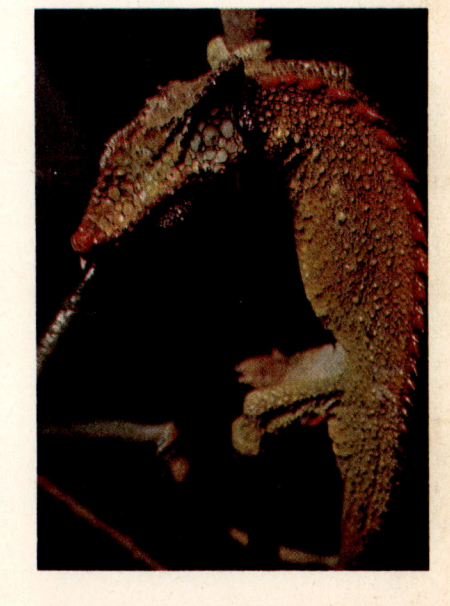

144 / ANIMAL TRAITS

(above)
Not all animals with **horns** use them as weapons; but the **bighorn ram** uses his as a battering device. Nevertheless, these curling horns serve more frequently as status symbols. The larger the ram and the bigger the horns, the less likely it is to be challenged by a smaller ram with smaller horns.

(above, right)
Sable antelopes have long, graceful scimitar-like **horns** up to 52 inches long. So great is their courage that they will not hesitate to attack a lion, and they are often victorious. Few of these creatures are alive today. A few hundred live in Angola, on government reservations.

herd tossed the lion with its horns to begin with, and the rest of the herd joined in to pass the lion from one set of horns to another, until finally it was allowed to fall to the ground, dead.

We can recall also the matadors that come to an untimely end by the horns of a bull, and others who have met the same fate from chance encounters with the males of this species of *Bovidae*. Even so, it is arguable whether these are primarily weapons, in the strict sense. Even if we accept that they are, we can turn to other members of the *Bovidae* in which the horns play little part. Aggression on the part of a goat takes the form of butting with the forehead. Most antelopes, which are members of the *Bovidae*, fail to use their horns defensively when faced with a predator such as a lion. The gemsbok and the sable will do so readily, and the wildebeest and other antelopes will do so to defend their young. But for most antelopes the horns seem to serve mainly as adornment.

This anomalous situation can be illustrated by the use of the horns by various species of rhinoceros. The powerful Indian rhinoceros strikes with its front teeth at an enemy, whereas the aggressive black rhino of Africa uses its horns. The Indian rhino has front teeth, or tushes, in both upper and lower jaws and those in the lower jaw project forwards. The black rhino has no teeth in its upper jaw, and consequently must use its horns or be without a weapon. This seems only explainable on the ground, as has already been suggested, that normally an animal uses whatever it finds itself possessed of in order to fight.

One purpose served by casting doubt on the function of teeth, claws, horns or antlers as weapons *per se*, even if it is possible to argue to the contrary, is that it points up the contrast between such general armament and the special weapons possessed by the minority. Primitive man took a risky step when, instead of relying on his nails and teeth for fighting, he picked up a stone and hurled it, or used a stick for striking an enemy. The stone and the stick thus became special weapons because that was the sole purpose for which they were used. Some animals with grasping hands do likewise.

Some Fight, Some Flee

WE ARE TOLD THAT BABOONS will throw stones at an intruder, or roll boulders down a slope on to him. There is no indication that they do this to other than human intruders, but that may be only because no one has so far been there to see it happen—or if they have they have kept the information to themselves. It has been observed that gorillas, in moments of anxiety, will tear off branches of foliage and throw them towards an intruder, but since they throw them at random the action would appear to be not so much an act of aggression as a sign of annoyance. Nevertheless, this may indicate an initial step towards the use of specific weapons, which has been taken a stage further in other species which actually aim at their adversaries. There seems to be something more deliberate than the random actions of gorillas in the way monkeys and chimpanzees in zoos will throw their own dung at visitors. And yet there is a very thin dividing line between the two actions. It is as though both sprang from an impulse to reach an adversary, no matter how ineffectively.

It would be vain to consider weapons and their possible uses without paying some attention to the instincts of "character" of the animal. It has been said that it is better for a herd of deer to be led by a lion than for a pride of lions to be led by a stag. As an allegory this may

(above, left)
Rhinoceros horns are formed from closely packed fibers and have no connection with the bone of the skull. The Asian species shown here can run quite fast, with a lumbering, earth-shattering tread. When confronted by man, it is more likely to run than to charge; and if it does charge, it often misses because of poor eyesight. Man is its only effective enemy, and many of the Asiatic species live in reservations for their protection.

(above, right)
The sharp-horned **black rhinoceros** is a massive fighter. In general it is peace-loving, but it can be alarmed easily, partly because of its poor vision. When it panics it usually charges upwind, and with a weight of up to 3,000 pounds behind the long tusk, it is a fearsome opponent.

146 / ANIMAL TRAITS

(below, left) Group-living has many advantages for a **baboon**. Besides companionship, they have protection against intruders. As many as fifty may live together in a well-defined community. Sentries guard against enemies and the powerful older males act as warriors.

(below, right) Few wild creatures use **tools** or have the ability to throw objects effectively. The **baboon**, however, can pick up sizable rocks and throw them hard enough to discourage approaching enemies.

have much to commend it, but to give a better example of the principle we could compare a green woodpecker and a magpie. Both are about the same size and both have beaks of similar power and striking potential. Yet the one seeks safety in flight and the other will readily attack. Furthermore, even if a woodpecker were cornered and sought to use its beak to defend itself, it would not show the fighting tactics of a magpie. When it has started to attack, a magpie delivers rapid and heavy blows, all the time moving rapidly about so that its repeated attacks seem to come from all directions. Moreover, once in a fighting mood, a magpie if forced to retreat does so still facing its adversary. It does not turn its back on its enemy, but is ready to come forward again with rapid, thrusting blows of its beak.

These are rapier thrusts in the truest sense, alternately coming in to seek the enemy's weaker points, then quickly retiring just out of reach, keeping the foe at arm's length to inflict the greatest damage on him while minimizing the damage to oneself. A logical extension of this is to use some form of projectile to inflict damage at a distance.

Successive steps taken by early man to inflict damage at a distance would have been to use the fists, to strike with a stick, to throw a stone, to use a sling, and finally to fire an arrow from a bow. From that stage man has progressed through the early cannon to the rifled barrel, and now to the intercontinental ballistic missile. Despite this breathtaking progress, however, man was not the first to use the principle of the projectile to reduce the possibility of personal injury by striking at an adversary over a distance.

WEAPONS / 147

A baboon can throw a stone because it has a grasping hand. A camel, when irritated, will eject its saliva at a person. We see it champing its jaws as if deliberately "working up" the saliva in order to collect a sufficient quantity to be effective. Then it draws its head back and, with a thrust forward, spits. Should this prove unavailing, the camel will then eject some of its stomach contents through the mouth, forcefully. The llama, a close relative of the camel, will do likewise.

Apart from the use of spitting as a sign of contempt, there is little indication that this form of aggression is at all widespread among modern man; yet it is reasonable to suppose it may have been a habit of early man, possibly springing from the same impulse that leads a gorilla to throw branches. Many animals, also, will vomit purely as a nervous reaction in moments of danger, but this has become systematized and taken to its extreme by the sea cucumber, which ejects the whole of its internal organs at an enemy and then grows a new set. It has been said that this is effective because a predator stops to eat these ejected parts and so allows the sea cucumber to escape, but it could also act as a deterrent.

(top, left)
The male **gorilla** has inspired terror, for he sometimes presents a frightening spectacle. He thumps his chest, roars and throws branches. At times he seems about to annihilate his foes. Then he suddenly stops, waits for his family to reach safety and then follows them.

(top, right)
Apart from sharks, killer whales and man, **dolphins** have few enemies. Extremely sensitive, playful creatures, their only defenses are in their speed and, if necessary, in the powerful thrusts they can make with their **"beaks"**.

(above, left)
Woodpeckers are cautious, invariably climbing around to the far side of the tree trunk when they are observed.

(above, right)
The **European magpie** is a master of combat. It attacks with swift thrusts of its strong **beak**.

148 / ANIMAL TRAITS

(right)
One particularly useful device that the **camel** has to combat difficult situations is its ability to discharge the contents of its stomach when it is irritated.

(below)
The long-legged **secretary bird** of South Africa kills snakes by stamping on them with its strong **toes** and sharp **claws.** In this picture we see the agility with which it can attack. Usually it hunts on foot, running rather than flying after its prey.

It is often difficult to draw the line between passive defensive techniques, such as would be represented by the ejection of the sea cucumber's viscera, and the use of special weapons, which is what these same viscera would be if they struck an enemy, causing him to retreat. A better example of this difficulty is seen in the armature of the hedgehog. Ordinarily it defends itself passively. At the approach of actual danger, or even of a potential threat such as an unusual sound, a hedgehog prepares to take refuge within its palisade of spines. When danger is imminent it rolls up completely and presents to the world an array of spines which are harmless to an intruder unless he presses home the attack. This, however, is not the end of this particular story, but it does raise the question of what constitutes a weapon, and some attempt should be made to answer this before proceeding further.

What Is a Weapon?

A DICTIONARY DEFINITION of "weapon" is "an instrument of offensive or defensive combat; something to fight with". The hedgehog's spines could be compared with a portcullis or a palisade of pointed stakes erected in front of earthworks, among obsolete human armaments, or even with a barbed wire entanglement as used in the more sophisticated trench warfare. All are defensive instruments used for combating enemies. Yet we do not usually regard these as weapons. However, if a body of men were to pull up the pointed stakes in a palisade and advance with them, points directed at an enemy, they would immediately become weapons in the full sense. Something of this sort happens in hedgehogs.

As we have seen, the normal role of the spines is purely passive. A more positive use of the spines as weapons is, however, seen in young hedgehogs during their first month or so of life, before they have developed the ability to roll up. At that time, when disturbed or alarmed, the young hedgehog jumps upwards repeatedly, on all

WEAPONS / 149

fours, to a height of two or three inches. To try picking up a baby hedgehog at that time can be a painful experience, when it jumps and the tips of the spines strike one's fingertips. It is easy to see also that a predator such as a fox or badger, investigating an infant hedgehog, might be deterred from further attack on receiving the tips of the spines on its sensitive nose.

Ivan Sanderson has claimed that the adult hedgehog may use this same form of attack, leaping a foot into the air. If this is correct, then the spines in that instant pass from a passive weapon, like the palisade in front of an earthworks, or the barbed wire, to an offensive weapon comparable with a pike, or a spiked mace as used by medieval knights.

There is something similar in the porcupine's methods of protecting itself. Its coat of quills, especially that of the crested porcupine, is a formidable but passive protection in the ordinary course of events. On occasion, however, a porcupine will run backwards at its enemy, and the barbed ends of the quills, piercing the skin, become detached and, by virtue of their barbs, work their way into the flesh of the porcupine's attacker with every movement it makes. This must be a painful process and there have been instances in which the quills have finally entered a vital organ, such as the heart, with fatal results. However, by that time the porcupine may have been dead for some days, so that as a means of survival the lethal nature of the quills would have been of little value to the porcupine.

There is a legend that a porcupine may shoot its quills, and if this were true it would represent a more positive attack, and the quills would then count more definitely as weapons, since they would be effective over a distance, so keeping the porcupine out of harm's way. It seems fairly certain now that this legend is not correct, or only half correct. Nevertheless, from reports given by careful observers it seems that, although the porcupine may not shoot its quills deliberately, it may thrash its tail and any loose quills may then be thrown a short

(above)
The exotically beautiful **jellyfish** known as the **Portuguese man-of-war** has a floating colony of polyps with long trailing **tentacles.** Each tentacle is armed with thousands of stinging cells that eject poison darts into the skin of anything that brushes against it. Any contact with the tentacles produces a fiery welt. A serious sting can be fatal.

(left)
When threatened the **porcupine** rushes backwards at its enemy, stabbing it with **quills** that may be as long as twenty inches. Loosely attached to the porcupine, the barbed quills pull off and remain in the enemy after the attack, which may prove fatal if certain vital organs are damaged.

150 / ANIMAL TRAITS

(above, left)
A **skunk** always gives warning before it attacks: it walks upright on its front legs. If the warning is ignored, it then ejects a stream of **acrid fluid** through its tail glands. Not only is the resulting **scent** abominable, but the fluid also burns, and temporary blindness may result. The jet of liquid may spray an area of up to twelve feet.

(above, right)
While the **weasel** can give off a foul odor, its defenses lie rather in avoiding combat and in the lightning speed with which it can move. A fierce and persistent hunter, it catches mice by following them into their burrows. It keeps well away from larger animals and seldom exposes itself to sight. If necessary, it can give a swift bite with its needle-sharp teeth.

distance, and such quills have been seen to become embedded in a log or wooden post a foot or two away, in the manner of arrows.

Even if the action is not deliberate or contemplated, the result would be to put the quill in the class of projectile weapons such as the sling, the arrow and the intercontinental missile. When one looks at the tail of the African brush-tailed porcupine, it is difficult to believe that the concentration of quills in a bunch at the end of the tail is entirely fortuitous. Although nobody has as yet recorded the tail itself being used as an offensive weapon, it seems likely that it could be; and it is even possible that the story, which we now count as legend, originated with this species rather than with the better-known species of porcupine.

When a skunk is alarmed it discharges a noxious fluid from its anal glands. This comes even nearer to the human concept of a projectile weapon. The scent of this fluid is highly repellent, and the fluid itself can be ejected to a distance of ten to twelve feet, even farther with a strong wind. It is also said to burn like acid on the skin and to cause temporary blindness. There is little difficulty in seeing this as a cross between a poison gas ejector and a flamethrower as used in human warfare. Without doubt this is an offensive weapon, in every sense.

The skunk belongs to the weasel family, and it is of interest to trace within this family what could have been the successive steps in the evolution of this weapon. The weasel and its larger relative, the stoat or ermine, both discharge a liquid from their anal glands in moments of excitement. It is foul-smelling, although it has nothing like the noxious qualities attributed to the skunk, and it cannot be ejected more than a foot or so at most.

The polecat or foul marten, another member of the weasel family, does likewise, and it is enough to quote the old saying, "To stink like a polecat", to see that its protective device is a step forward towards that of the skunk. The pine marten, a close relative of the polecat, also has this same propensity for giving off a strong scent, but this animal is

(above)
The nine-banded armadillo is well insulated from most of its natural enemies. When frightened it rolls into a ball, protected by the **bony armor** of its back. It can also swiftly dig a hole to hide in. Of its enemies, the most dangerous is the souvenir hunter.

(left)
Unable to burrow, the **three-banded armadillo** is almost defenseless. All it can do is to roll itself up into a ball.

known as the sweet marten, because although its scent is sickly-sweet it does not have the same offensive effect as the discharge from a polecat. The badgers also eject a liquid from these glands. In the European badger it has the smell of musk, sickly-sweet but not overpowering, but the honey badger of South-east Asia uses its discharge much as the skunk does.

In all members of the weasel family the discharge is triggered by a nervous reflex, and may occur not only in moments of alarm but, in some species, also in moments of contentment or pleasure. The musk of the European badger is most in evidence during courtship, for example.

If there is a doubt how far these various discharges from the anal glands, as used by other members of the weasel family, can be accepted as true weapons, there is no doubt about how the skunks use theirs. A skunk will whip its body into a U-shape so that it can see the target, and presumably there is some jockeying for position and taking of deliberate aim. So within the weasel family there is a transition from the random discharge of a fluid, the result of a nervous reflex, to a deliberate aiming at a target, the latter constituting beyond doubt a use of the anal glands as a positive weapon.

It might be argued that something resulting from a nervous reflex does not come, strictly speaking, within the definition of a weapon. It is, therefore, worth considering how far the outer half of a lizard's tail can be treated as one. Although this may appear at first sight to be far removed from the skunk's discharge, or that of other members of the weasel family, there is some similarity in the end achieved. That is, it is a means of protection. It is usually said that if you seize a lizard by its tail the outer half will be cast and the lizard will grow a replacement; but the situation is not nearly as simple as that. A tame lizard will allow itself to be held by the tail without casting it. But a lizard, wild or tame, sensing danger, will cast its tail even if the tail is not touched. The cast portion of the tail then bounces and bounds about in such a spectacular manner that it catches and holds one's attention. There can be no doubt it would hold the attention of a predator in the same way. Meanwhile, the lizard itself quickly and silently glides into cover—and safety.

The casting of the tail is due to a nervous reflex. It is therefore involuntary. The action may satisfy one part of the dictionary definition in that it is a defensive instrument.

The action of the skunk in ejecting a noxious fluid and of directing it at a target is paralleled by several others that are, if anything, even more remarkable. Probably the most familiar are the spitting cobras, which is the name given to several species. The best-known is the rintchals, of South Africa. This snake can spit its venom to a distance of seven feet and is said to direct it accurately at the face and eyes of an

(below, left)
The joey, or young **gray kangaroo,** finds refuge in the mother's pouch, where it is guarded by her powerful **hind feet.** These are armed with strong claws that will rip an enemy open. Some male kangaroos are capable of killing a man by balancing on their tails and kicking with their hind legs.

(below, center)
The **grass snake** without venom has three means of protection. It may strike at an enemy with its teeth, which is a bluff because the teeth are harmless. It can also give off an unpleasant scent. If these two tactics fail, it will turn over on its back with mouth open and tongue lolling, looking quite dead, as the picture shows.

(below, right)
Although many antelopes seem to have horns only for decoration, the **sable antelope** sometimes uses its horns for defensive purposes.

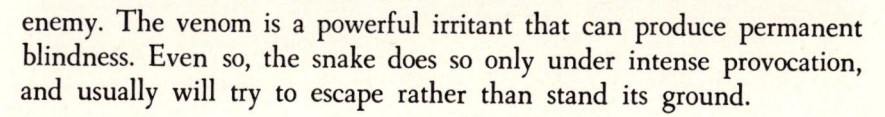

enemy. The venom is a powerful irritant that can produce permanent blindness. Even so, the snake does so only under intense provocation, and usually will try to escape rather than stand its ground.

Defended by Blood

ONE OF THE ODDEST EXAMPLES of this form of self-protection occurs in the reptile known as the "horned toad" living in the deserts of the south-western United States. When alarmed, this lizard may squirt a few drops of blood from its eyes for several feet. A highly complicated system for increasing blood pressure in the head, common to all reptiles, combined with an extremely thin-walled eye membrane, makes this possible in the horned lizard. The blood is said to be an irritant if it enters the eyes of small mammals, and if this is true, then it would be as good a deterrent as the venom of the spitting cobra, although it is not projected over so great a distance. Perhaps the more remarkable feature is that a desert animal should sacrifice even a small amount of body fluid, because usually all the adaptations of a desert-living animal are towards conserving body fluids owing to the difficulty of obtaining water to replace them. Yet there is another type of desert animal that does something very similar.

Living in the deserts of Africa is a kind of bush cricket which squirts blood from its legs. On each of the thigh joints of the first and middle legs, between those parts of the leg known as the coxa and the trochanter, is a pore. The bush cricket can squirt twin jets of blood at an enemy, and in doing so it moves about until it is in the correct position to send the jets into the face and eyes of an enemy, usually a lizard. In this instance also the blood is said to have a caustic quality.

There are a number of other insects in which the blood has caustic properties and is discharged in small drops when the insect is seized. This is known as reflex bleeding. Usually the blood oozes from around the joints of the legs, but in some species it is given out from other parts of the body. In the bloody-nose beetle it is given out from the

(above, left)
The **horned toad** is actually a reptile living in the deserts of the southwestern United States and Mexico. When disturbed it squirts blood through its eyes, which seems to act as a repellent to small mammals.

(above, right)
The unique Galapagos archipelago, or island group, has produced many specialized creatures, such as the **scarlet crab**. The crab squirts water at any intruder; and, more remarkable, so does the marine iguana with which it lives.

154 / ANIMAL TRAITS

*The **snapping turtle**, a North American fresh-water turtle, is not one to withdraw into its shell. When attacked, it lunges at the enemy, biting it savagely. Although it has no teeth, the turtle's jaws can give a powerful bite.*

*By using its proboscis, a contracting tube with a pointed end, the **marine worm** buries itself in the sand, forcing its way through. With the hooklike jaws at the end of the tube it captures other marine worms as well as crustaceans and mollusks. Its jaws, however, are used only for holding; they cannot tear the victim, which has to be swallowed whole.*

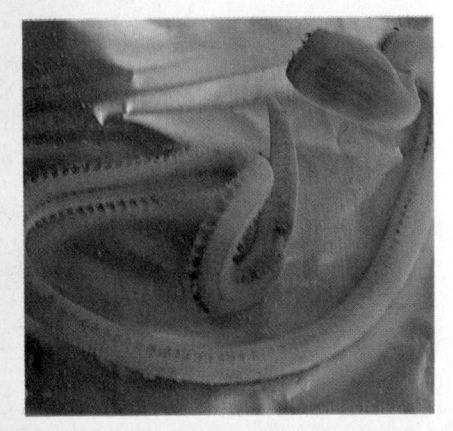

mouth and is bright red. The devil's coach-horse, also of Europe, is a beetle with small wing cases and a long flexible abdomen. When alarmed it brings the hind part of its body up and over its back, so that the tip of the abdomen is pointed in the same direction as its head. At the same time it opens its jaws wide. This threatening attitude is followed, if an attack is pressed home, by the beetle's giving off a fetid scent from glands near the vent.

On the Galapagos Islands live marine iguanas that spend much of their time basking on the rocks, but go into the sea to feed on seaweeds. There is a red crab that lives with the iguanas, which climbs on to the iguanas when they are basking and picks the ticks off their skin. The iguana will squirt water from its mouth at an enemy. The red crab also squirts water, from its gill chambers, at an enemy. It is a remarkable coincidence that two such dissimilar animals, living side by side, should have this same habit.

These several examples recall the archer fish, which takes deliberate aim at a fly and then spits at it a stream of droplets of water. This eight-inch fish lives in fresh and brackish waters, from India to the Philippines, and the first accurate account of what it does was given as far back as 1765. This was treated with scepticism for well over a century, but later research, together with high-speed photography, has now set the matter beyond doubt.

The fish aims at flies and spiders crawling over vegetation overhanging the water. If you dip a stick in water it looks bent at the point where it enters the water. This is due to refraction. When a fish looks up through water an object in the air beyond that appears to be in a straight line with its mouth would, in fact, be away to the side of this line. The archer fish, when about to shoot at an insect, deliberately takes up position as near the vertical as possible beneath the insect. This reduces to the minimum the effects due to refraction.

There is a groove in the palate of the archer fish, and at the moment of firing the tongue is pressed upwards, converting the groove into a tube; the gill covers are drawn in sharply, and water in the gill chambers is driven forcefully up the tube, sending a stream of water a distance of up to four feet. This knocks the insect down on the surface of the water, where the archer fish seizes it.

Although the archer fish has been called Nature's machine gun, its actions are used to obtain food, which keeps them outside the strict definition of a weapon. This is as well, because if food-getting instruments were to be admitted as weapons we should have to deal with a whole range of snares, especially the webs made by spiders. Nevertheless, perhaps one spider at least should be mentioned. This is the bolas spider, which spins a silk thread with a knob of silk at the end. Seated on its web the spider casts this at a passing fly. If the aim misses, the thread is hauled in ready for another shot.

There is, however, one spider which has a means of defending itself that should qualify as a true weapon of sorts. This is a bird-eating spider which is said to scrape its hairy abdomen with its hind legs, releasing clouds of fine dust which baffle and stifle its pursuer. This bears some resemblance to the ink cloud thrown out by a cuttlefish, octopus or squid, in which the effect is not only to provide a means of escape from an enemy, but also, in squids, to act as a decoy. The squid throws out its ink, which for a moment remains concentrated. During that time, and before the ink has had time to disperse, the squid turns so pale as to be almost transparent and darts rapidly away, leaving the predator attacking the blob of ink.

The use of venom has been mentioned already, as in the spitting cobra, and although few animals are capable, like that snake, of delivering venom at an enemy over a distance, a very large number use it not only as a means of obtaining food but as a form of passive protection. In a few instances, the manner in which the venom is employed has the appearance of an offensive weapon used in unprovoked attack. What is meant here is best illustrated by the poison "teeth" of certain cone shells.

The majority of mollusks are either vegetarian or feed on small particles of dead animal and plant matter. Most, also, have no means of protection apart from their shells. The vegetarians obtain their food by rasping away vegetable matter with a radula, often called a tongue. In its simplest form this is a horny ribbon beset by numerous small horny teeth, and it is used like a file. In many instances the teeth are of different sizes and shapes, and they not only cut the food up fine but

Bird-eating spiders make frequent and unwelcome appearances at banana warehouses and ports. Although they are greatly feared, they rarely use their venom, and when they do, its effect is no more serious than that of a bee sting. In capturing birds, however, it is a different matter, for the spiders can overcome them by sheer strength. They are also clever at avoiding enemies, throwing up their own dust screens to confuse pursuers.

(left)
In appearance the **rhinoceros beetle** is solid as an army tank. But it is doubtful that the formidable horns on its head (which give it its name) have very much value as weapons. At most they are used by the males in trials of strength.

156 / ANIMAL TRAITS

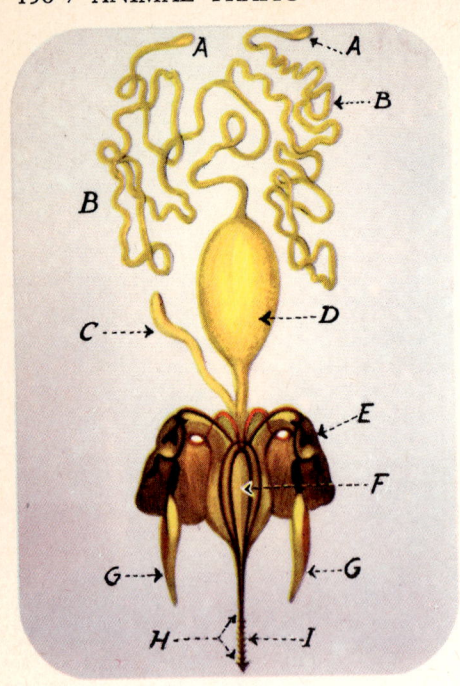

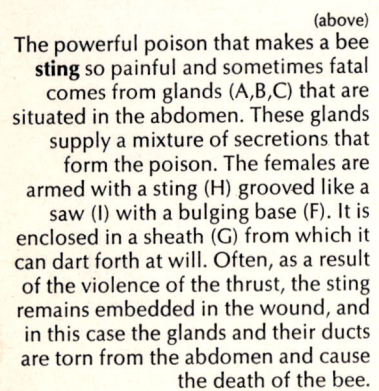

(above)
The powerful poison that makes a bee **sting** so painful and sometimes fatal comes from glands (A,B,C) that are situated in the abdomen. These glands supply a mixture of secretions that form the poison. The females are armed with a sting (H) grooved like a saw (I) with a bulging base (F). It is enclosed in a sheath (G) from which it can dart forth at will. Often, as a result of the violence of the thrust, the sting remains embedded in the wound, and in this case the glands and their ducts are torn from the abdomen and cause the death of the bee.

(above)
The treacherous **beak** with its sharp teeth is used by the **sawfish** to grub about in the mud for food. It is also used for attacking a shoal of fish swimming in the water by striking rapidly from side to side, stunning and killing its victims. The sawfish may attack larger fish, cutting lumps from their flesh.

since some of them are movable also act like pincers to grip the fragments and draw them into the mouth. There are, however, some carnivorous mollusks, such as the whelk, in which the radula is capable of boring through the shell of another mollusk, and then of rasping away the soft body inside.

In the cone shell, another carnivorous mollusk, the radula is reduced to a few teeth only, and only one is functional at a time. It has a barbed tip and there is a poison sac associated with it, by means of which it is able to sting and overpower its prey. Cone shells carry an attractive pattern and are as a consequence much prized by collectors, one of them, *Conus gloriamaris,* being the greatest prize and worth something in the region of $850 for a single shell. But as sometimes happens in other spheres of life, this beauty is not without its drawbacks, and collectors of live cone shells have been known to be stung in the hand, sometimes fatally.

When the tooth of a cone shell is used, the barbed tip causes it to remain fixed in the tissues of a victim. If the victim is large and strong the tooth may be torn away, in which event one of the several spare teeth moves in to replace it.

Bees, Wasps and Ants

THE MANNER OF USE of this poisoned barb recalls the more familiar, and less harmful, sting of the honeybee. In a hive there are a queen and drones, and a large number, up to 60,000, of sterile females or workers. The queen uses her sting only on rival queens. It is not barbed, so it can be withdrawn and used more than once. The sting of a worker bee is, however, barbed and cannot be withdrawn. Consequently, when a worker bee stings an intruder, whether a human or an animal, the sting is left behind, as the bee seeks to disengage itself, together with parts of the bee's vital organs. The result, for the bee, is death. This is a remarkable state of affairs, in which the use of a weapon automatically becomes an act of suicide. It can only be supposed that the barb is an accessory that holds the sting long enough in the wound to ensure the maximum injection of venom. The primary purpose of a weapon is the protection of the individual, but in a society such as that of the honeybees, the sacrifice of an individual may ensure survival to its fellows. In any event, the number of occasions on which bees in the wild are called upon to use their weapons on enemies must be very small.

Wasps are less hindered in their offensive actions. Their sting is unbarbed, and a wasp can deliver a dozen thrusts in as many minutes and still survive.

Bees, wasps and ants are closely related, but whereas the first two have a sting, which is a modified ovipositor (the workers being, as we have seen, sterile females), most ants protect their nests or themselves by the use of formic acid, or similar acrid fluids, ejected from the hind end of the abdomen. When the wall of a large nest is disturbed, as when the top of the nest of the large European wood ant is knocked off, in no time at all the workers will line the breach. Each can be seen with its abdomen brought forward under the body, and directed towards the focus of the disturbance. If you hold your hand near the broken ramparts the jets of formic acid strike the skin, producing a sensation very like that known as "pins and needles", which is felt after the hand has been numbed and is returning to normal. At the same time the air

(below, left)
As many as one million ants may inhabit a single **ant hill.** Usually the hill is developed in a shaded area and contains extensive underground chambers to accommodate the highly complex life style of an ant colony. When disturbed, workers immediately come to the defense, shooting formic acid at the attackers.

(below)
Ants have three methods of obtaining food: gathering, hunting and growing. Sharp jaws are useful for hunting and dragging food home and also for injecting the poison that some ants carry. In the tropics certain ants have become nomadic. Colonies of as many as 100,000 ants set out as a horde, attacking any unfortunate creature that crosses their path.

becomes filled with the overpowering smell of formic acid, which irritates the throat and causes coughing. Some birds seem not only to be immune to the effects of formic acid but to positively enjoy it. There must, nevertheless, be many enemies of ants which would be repulsed by it.

The little black ant of Europe has a double weapon. In attacking human beings, and presumably other enemies, it bites and at the same time squirts formic acid into the wound. The result is far more unpleasant than either the bite or the formic acid on its own.

Most insects have no sting and the majority use no poison except such as may be contained in the unpleasant taste they can inflict on anything trying to eat them. Those in the latter category are remarkable enough, since they include such insects as the burnet moths, whose bodies contain prussic acid. There are other insects to which we commonly attribute the ability to sting, notably the mosquitoes, but theirs is a bite, the irritation we experience from it being due, so it is believed, to the injection into the bite of the insect's saliva. Moreover, there is no question here of a weapon, because a mosquito bites to suck our blood, the rest being subsidiary; the insect does not attack aggressively, nor is it protecting itself.

The termites, the so-called white ants of the tropics, have of all insects carried the use of an offensive weapon to its extreme. In any colony of termites there is more than one caste, and in some species there may be several, including soldiers, as indeed there are in some species of ants. The usual soldier termite has a large head armed with powerful jaws. When a hole is made in the wall of the termitarium, the soldiers move into the breach to defend it. In some species the large head of the soldier may be used to block up the hole in the wall of the nest until it can be repaired.

In a few species of termites some of the soldiers are even more specially developed. Known as nasutes, each has a beak, sometimes quite long, and when an invader breaks into a termitarium the nasutes gather at the threatened point. From the long beak is exuded a drop, or a jet, of toxic fluid, which can be disastrous to other insects. The nasutes are, in fact, living weapons, because they cannot feed themselves, and have to be fed by the worker termites.

The Uses of Poison

How widespread is the use of poisons can best be illustrated by starting at the lowest animals and working upward through the animal scale. Among the lower animals we find the group known as the coelenterates, a name which means "hollow stomachs". But as all members of the group are equipped with stinging cells they are often referred to collectively as the nettle animals. The coelenterates include such well-known animals as jellyfishes and sea anemones, corals and

(opposite)
The **Atlas beetle,** found throughout Indonesia, has armor-plating unmatched by any other insect. The stout horn on the head rises upward and is bent back at the tip. In some species there is a tooth in the middle of the horn.

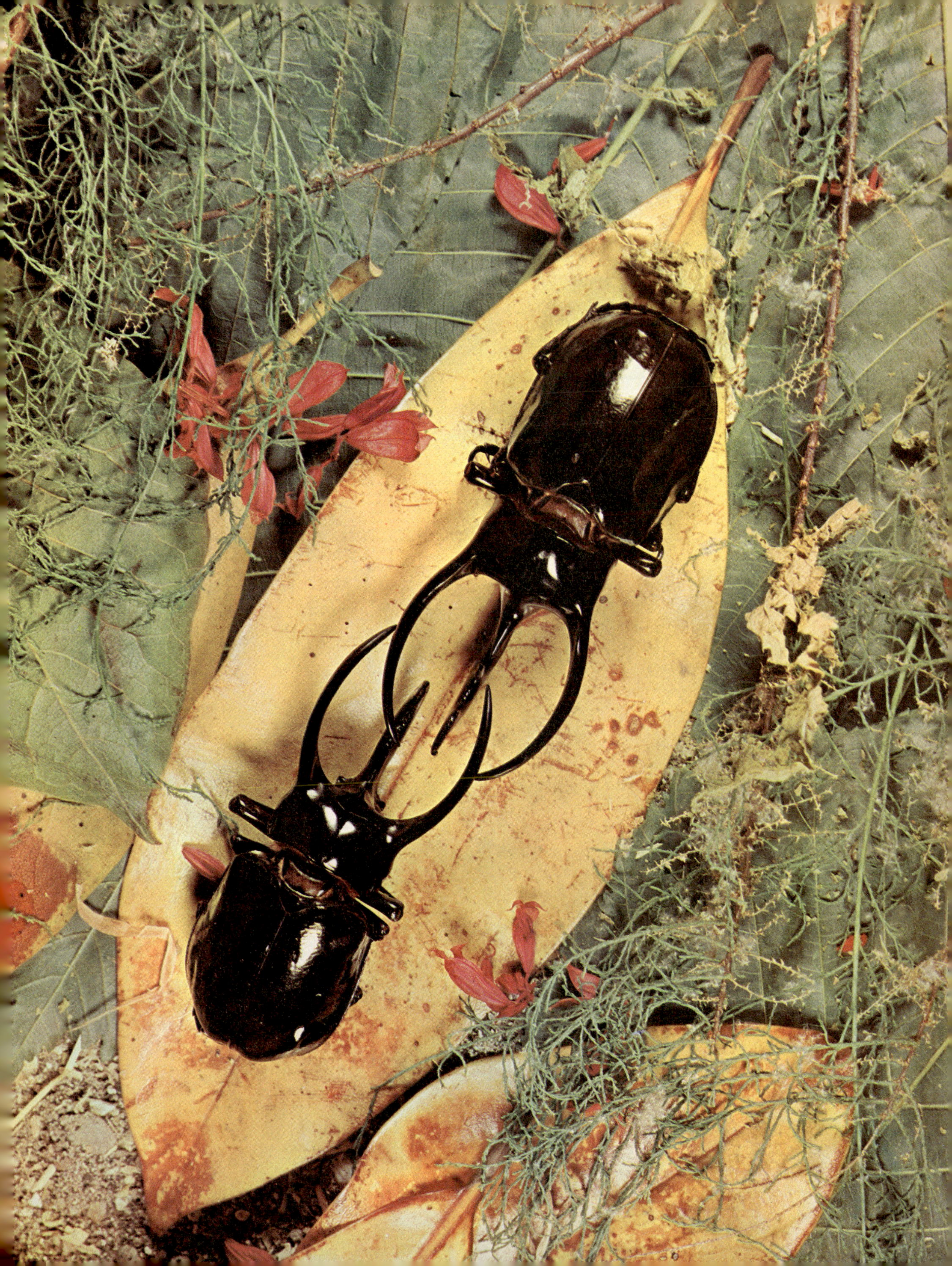

ANIMAL TRAITS

false corals, but it includes others less well known, such as sea firs and sea pens. All have nematocysts, or stinging cells, and for our present purpose we need only consider a typical nematocyst, together with some of the more notorious carriers.

Primarily the nematocyst is a means of obtaining food, but secondarily it is defensive, although there are few coelenterates, even those with the most virulent stings, that are not eaten by one animal or another which seem to be immune to the poison. Where a coelenterate does deliver an injurious or fatal attack, other than on its prey species, this is largely fortuitous. It is the result of an animal, or a human being, accidentally coming into contact with its tentacles.

The most notorious of the coelenterates are the jellyfishes. So far as human beings are concerned the injury is to a large extent directly proportional to the size of the jellyfish. We can handle a small jellyfish with no obvious ill effects, just as we can handle a sea anemone's tentacles without discomfort, although we can feel the effect of the stinging cells entering our skin by the way the tentacles drag across our fingers.

Of all jellyfishes the one with the worst reputation in most parts of the world is that known as the Portuguese man-of-war, but often called by the anglicized version of its scientific name, physalia. It is a colony of polyps, one of which forms an elongated bladder or float which rides the surface of the sea like a miniature of the ships of war used by the Portuguese in the Middle Ages. Beneath this float hang numerous digestive and reproductive polyps, and also a number of tentacles, several feet long, armed with thousands of nematocysts.

Each nematocyst is of microscopic size. It consists of a single cell,

(below)
The moving **tentacles** at the mouth (1) of the **sea anemone** are armed with thousands of **stinging cells,** each microscopic in size. These cells go into action as the result of an ingenious mechanism. Each cell has a spike that, when pressed, acts as a trigger, shooting out a thin hollow tube that penetrates the skin of the victim and allows the poison to enter. The body of the anemone (2) rests on one foot that forms a kind of suction cup (3,4).

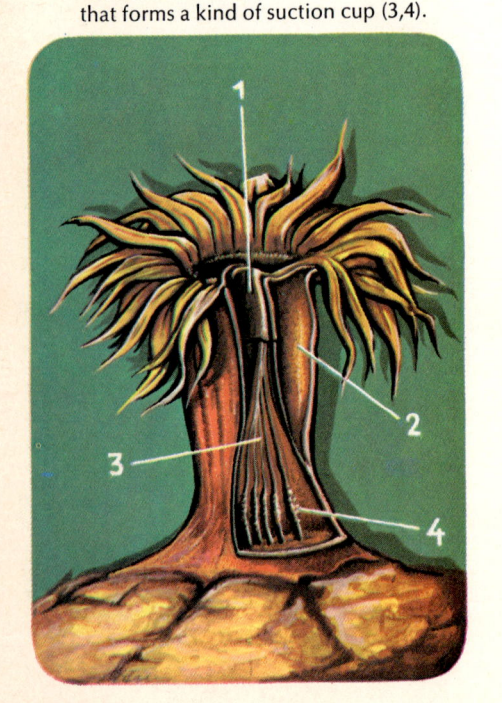

(below)
A **scorpion's sting** is in its tail, which it instinctively arches forward over its head whenever it is disturbed. Although this attitude is threatening, a scorpion does not sting unless it is severely provoked.

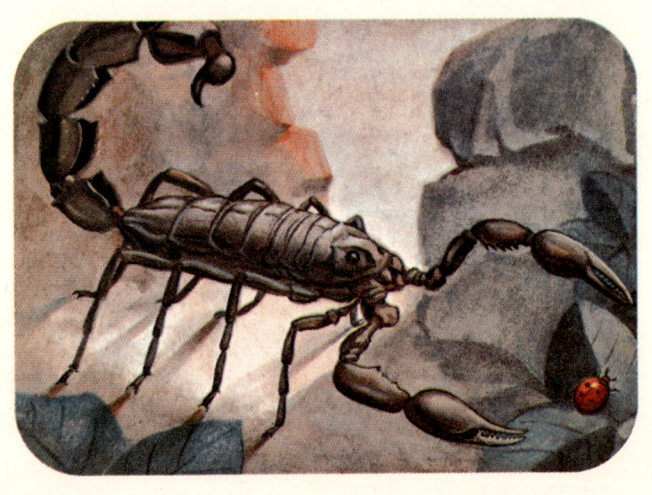

(left)
Sea urchins are covered with **spines**. These are effective weapons, especially when moved toward an approaching enemy. When a hand is extended across it, all the spines swing in the direction of the hand. Apparently nerve receptors receive the message that danger is near because of the change in the brightness of the light that passes over it. And so, in a way, the urchin can "see" the moving object.

(above)
The name **tarantula** is commonly used for any large hairy spider. Its dangerous reputation comes from a 17th century myth. A victim of a tarantula bite was said to be driven mad by it. The dance provoked by the madness survives to this day, and is known as the "tarantella." Fortunately, however, although the bite is poisonous it is not usually fatal. Tarantulas feed on earthworms, mice and small lizards, which they overcome by strength alone.

loaded with poison, and inside the cell is a long coiled tube. At the surface of the cell is a tiny spike. When this spike is touched it triggers the internal mechanism. The long threadlike tube is everted. That is, it is turned inside out, like the finger of a glove being drawn off clumsily. It penetrates the skin of whatever has touched the spike, and poison flows down it. The effect of one nematocyst would hardly be noticed, but for a bather to have the misfortune of coming into contact with one or more of the tentacles of a physalia, so receiving the poison from hundreds or thousands of nematocysts, is another matter entirely. He will find his body marked with red welts. The irritation from these is bad enough, but the later symptoms, in extreme cases, include difficulty with breathing and cramp in the muscles. The marks of the sting may persist for weeks.

Physalia abounds in the warmer seas, but its reputation is most evil in Australian waters, where it is known as the bluebottle, from the deep blue tinge on parts of its float. However, it is doubtful whether physalia has ever been responsible for the death of a person. Fatal cases have been reported, mainly among children, but there is a tendency on the part of those who have investigated the matter to believe that physalia is taking the blame for stings inflicted by boxjellies, known as sea wasps. Whereas physalia is a floating colony of polyps, a box-jelly is a single individual, closely related to the umbrella-shaped common jellyfish but shaped like a box (i.e. cuboid).

Among other marine invertebrates the use of venom is exceptional. There is at least one marine worm that is venomous. The spines of some sea urchins are poisonous, and bathers in the warmer waters of the world, getting these in the feet, have sustained excruciatingly painful wounds, which at times have been known to have fatal consequences.

Among land invertebrates poisonous insects have already been discussed. Their near relatives, the spiders and centipedes, are commonly equipped with poison glands associated with their fangs, which with rare exceptions are used to kill prey. The black widow spider steals the limelight on account of its virulent poison, which can be fatal to human beings, and some of the large tropical centipedes are best given a wide berth. Another spider, the tarantula of the legend, was believed to inject a poison causing a dancing mania named tarantism. The name tarantula is today applied to any large hairy spider, especially the bird-eating spiders of the tropics, which are relatively harmless, except to the small animals they prey upon.

Within the last few years a group of American scientists have made a definitive study of the manner in which centipedes discharge their prussic acid poison. The centipede has a row of pores along each side of the body. Just inside each pore is a tube leading to two small compartments separated by a valve. One compartment contains the chemical which can be converted into prussic acid. The other contains an enzyme capable of making this conversion. When a leg of the centipede is touched the valve in the poison gland nearest it opens, the prussic acid base and the enzyme flow together, and come out through the pore to the surface of the body in the form of a droplet of prussic acid. If the centipede is handled all the pores come into action. The result of this elegant poison-producing apparatus is that the centipede itself is unharmed by its own poison, since prussic acid is not formed until the liquid is outside the body.

The ability to climb perilous cliffs is an important factor in the survival of the **mountain goat.** It easily leaps about peaks where other animals dare not follow. Sometimes, if left unprotected, a small goat is taken by an eagle, one of the few creatures that can share his lofty habitat.

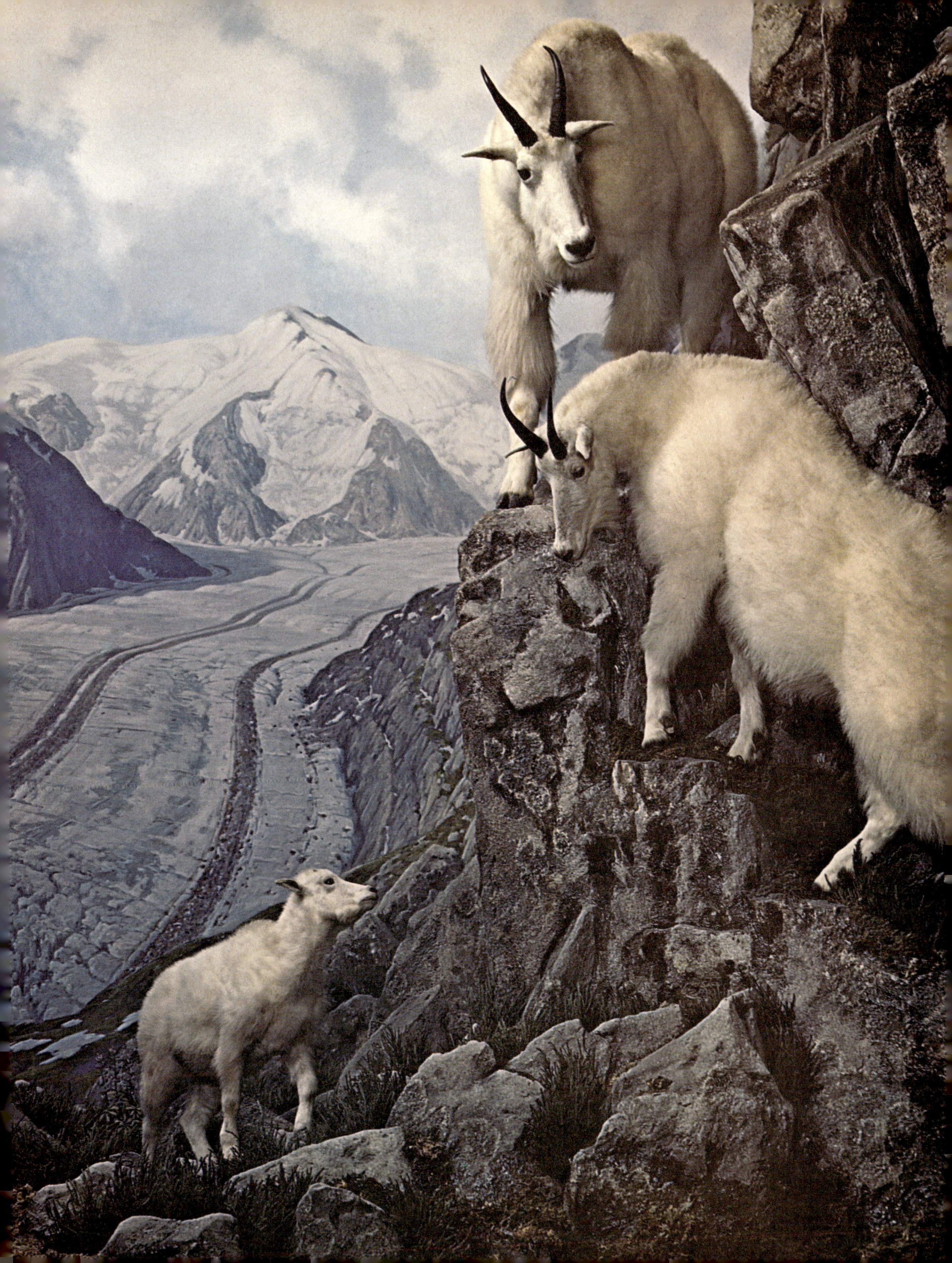

164 / ANIMAL TRAITS

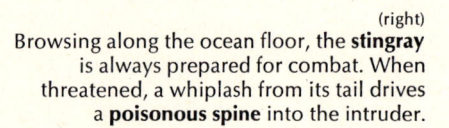

(right)
Browsing along the ocean floor, the **stingray** is always prepared for combat. When threatened, a whiplash from its tail drives a **poisonous spine** into the intruder.

(above)
The writhing **tentacles** of the **octopus** are armed with numerous suckers that enable it to wrap itself around an enemy or victim until the prey can be subjected to the strong, horny beak at its center. When in a defensive position the octopus can throw out a cloud of **ink** to escape from a foe.

Finally, among the invertebrates, there are the scorpions, with the sting in the tail, too well known to need description.

Leaving the invertebrates, we come to the fishes, and among these are many which use a venom. Outstanding are the spiny dogfishes, bullheaded sharks, eagle rays and chimaeras or rabbit fishes. These all belong to the type of fishes having cartilaginous skeletons. In them, a spine or spines somewhere on the body, but usually associated with the dorsal fins, is covered with tissue containing a poison. Such spines are very largely defensive, and inflict a poisonous wound only when the fish is handled. The stingray has a more offensive weapon: a flattened spine on the tail, toothed along each edge. Along each margin of the spine is a groove in which fits a glistening white tissue containing poison. The spine projects from about midway along a whiplike tail. When alarmed the stingray lashes its tail, thus driving the spine into any body with which it comes into contact.

Among the bony, or true, fishes, are the stonefishes, weevers, catfishes and toadfishes, all of which are poisonous. The name "weever" is derived from an old French word meaning viper, and the symptoms from its sting are much like those from snake-bite: fainting, palpitations, fever, delirium, vomiting, or even, in severe cases, heart failure. Yet in all these, the injury results either from handling the fish, or from stepping on one when bathing, the venom being delivered through hollow spines usually associated with the dorsal fin.

The amphibians, the next in ascending order among the vertebrates, include toads and salamanders, both with poison glands in the skin. These animals do not inject their poison, however, and it is only effective when an animal seizes a toad or salamander in the mouth. A dog picking up a toad between its teeth soon drops it. Almost immediately there is intense salivation. Saliva flows from the mouth and drips from the jaws, and the dog looks very sorry for itself. This may be followed by vomiting, and, in a small animal, death may ensue. Scientists who have experimentally taken a toad or salamander between the teeth report also a nausea and headaches, in addition to the salivation and vomiting.

Poisonous reptiles are almost exclusively snakes, but they include also the Gila monster and the beaded lizard of the south-western United States, the only two poisonous lizards. The fangs of venomous snakes are either hollow or grooved, permitting thus the flow of poison from a gland in the mouth to the body of the victim.

There are no birds that use a poison as a weapon, although some of the very bright-hued birds may have a skin that is unpalatable to some flesh eaters, but as yet there is only the scantiest of information on this, and for all practical purposes we can set all birds aside as non-venomous. Among mammals, the male platypus has spurs on the hind legs that discharge a poison, although to what use these are put has yet to be discovered; and some shrews use a poison. In most shrews the poison, when present, is in glands on the body, and only operates, like the poison of the toad, in a defensive role, but the short-tailed shrew of North America has poison glands at the bases of its lower incisors and these teeth project forward to form a groove along which the poison flows. This shrew can, therefore, inflict a poisonous bite. A mouse bitten by a short-tailed shrew will die of the poison, so it seems that the venom in this instance is used more for disabling prey than as an offensive weapon.

A unique weapon possessed by about 250 different species of fishes is the electric organ. In the torpedo ray the large muscles on either side of the body, in the flattened pectoral fins, are converted to electric cells. The freshwater electric catfish of Africa is perhaps less well known than the electric eels of South America. In it the electric organ envelops the whole body of the fish as a loose, semi-transparent jacket, capable of generating 350 to 450 volts, against the 40 volts of the electric torpedo. The maximum for the electric eels, which although

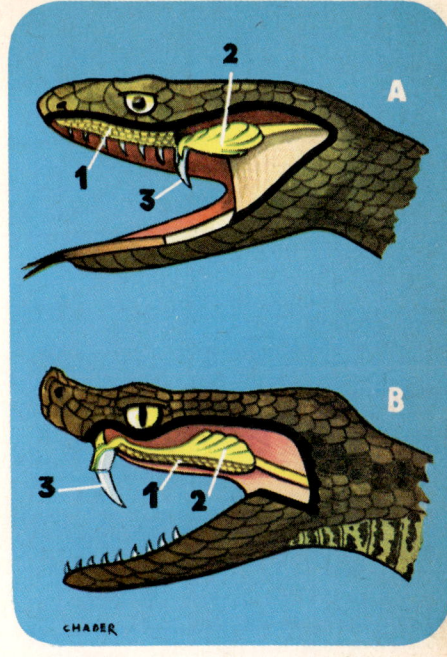

(above, left)
The South American **electric eel** is actually an eel-shaped fish. Using electric organs located in its tail, it can convey a severe electric shock, immobilizing or killing an opponent.

(above)
In both the **grass snake** (A) and the **viper** (B) venom is conveyed by means of a labial gland (1) and a venom gland (2). The hollow or grooved **fang** (3) allows the poison to be carried into the body.

eel-shaped are not eels but are related to carps, is 550 volts. These fishes have three electric organs on each side of the body, and together these occupy about half the mass of the body.

In conclusion, the most remarkable of all animal defensive weapons is found in certain sea slugs. They feed on sea firs and other nettle animals. Not only are they immune to the poison, apparently, but as the tissues of their prey are digested the nematocysts from them are unharmed. Furthermore, they migrate through the wall of the sea slug's stomach and up to its skin. There they become positioned in the skin ready to be discharged at the sea slug's enemies. A most remarkable example of "using the enemy's guns", one which remains unexplained.

ANIMAL WORLD

Perhaps one price of our modern civilization is that man has so separated and removed himself from the world of animals, as from nature in general, that he has become oblivious to its rhythms and insensitive to its subtlety and even—at times—its very existence. Yet if we are to restore our appreciation of the wholeness of life and recapture a true sense of wonder, we must delve more deeply into the secrets of this wide realm. And doing so, we will find that nature is not so mysterious at all, but that animals accomplish their work much as we do, move about in ways we can understand (if not always copy) and leave in their wake a detailed record of their progress and actions.

Over the course of history men have dreamed up inventions which would have defied the imaginations of those living in previous ages. In INVENTIONS IN NATURE we discover, however, that nearly all of these devices, from the simplest to the most intricate, exist in some form in the natural world. Indeed, faced with tasks and problems of existence that parallel our own, nature has often shown greater ingenuity than has technological, efficiency-oriented man. While most of our past inventions have been developed independently, there is a greater tendency today to look to nature for new ideas and for improvements.

From the lightning swiftness of the cheetah to the slow-motion of the sloth and from the lumbering elephant to the "swimming" one-celled protozoan, movement from place to place is an essential characteristic of the entire animal kingdom. When the need to move arises, animals use their muscles, feet, fins, flippers, suckers, wings or whatever they may have to get about as best they can, whether by wriggling or walking, swimming or flying. NATURE IN MOTION explores all the varied forms of movement which, taken together, constitute that flurry of activity we often observe in the air, on land and in the water.

Men write books about the things they have done and seek to memorialize them in art, but animals tell their stories on mud and snow, on brush and vegetation, where a change in the weather, another creature or the action of time itself is forever wiping out the old records and making way for new ones. TRACKS AND TRAILS seeks to open our eyes to this ephemeral "literature" so that we may expand our awareness of everything that goes on around us. For animals, whatever differences divide their world from ours, are yet our coinhabitants on this earth.

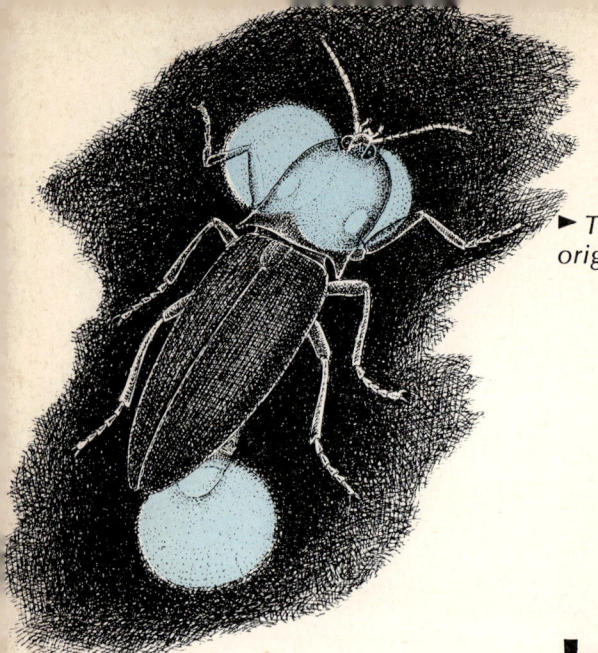

▶ *Techniques and tools developed and employed by man but originating in natural abilities possessed by animals.*

Inventions in Nature

THERE IS A KIND OF INSECT known as the whirligig beetle. These beetles are found almost everywhere in the world on shaded pools, in quiet corners of lakes or in the backwaters of rivers. They are small, blue-black or dark bronze, with oval flattened bodies. Insignificant on their own, they catch the eye when in a group by the way they whirl and spin, weaving in and out of the group, on the surface of the water. This is not their only claim to fame, however. Rather it is that they enjoy the best of three worlds: they are equally at home in the air, on the water or under the water.

Although a whirligig beetle spends most of its time gyrating on the surface of the water, it can also fly from one pond to another. Arriving over a suitable pond it drops down gently, using its wings now as a parachute to make a gentle landing. Should it need to dive it takes with it, under its wing-covers, a bubble of air. Returning to the surface it uses its rear two pairs of legs, which are flattened and oarlike, for sculling over the surface.

From the earliest tools to the most complicated machinery, man has arrived at his inventions independently, and yet almost everything he has come up with can be found in some form in the animal world. It is only recently that we have begun to look to the animal kingdom for new ideas or improvements. (top right) An **ichneumon fly** makes a derrick out of its body and drills with great precision. (top, far right) Using its beak as a chisel, a **woodpecker** hammers it into the wood of a dead tree.

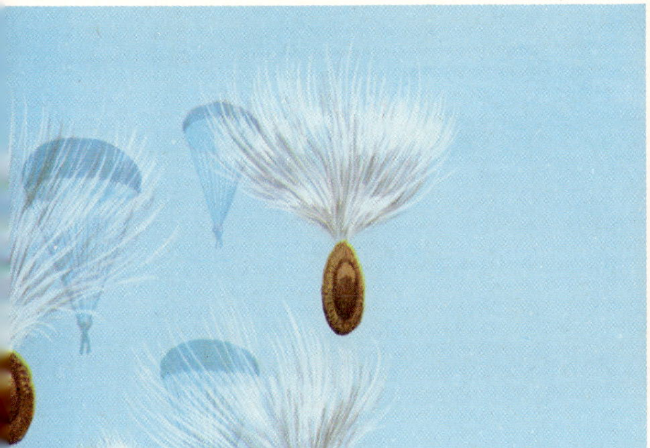

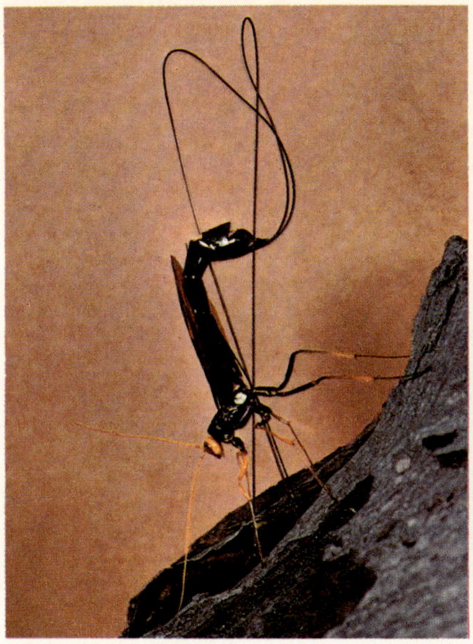

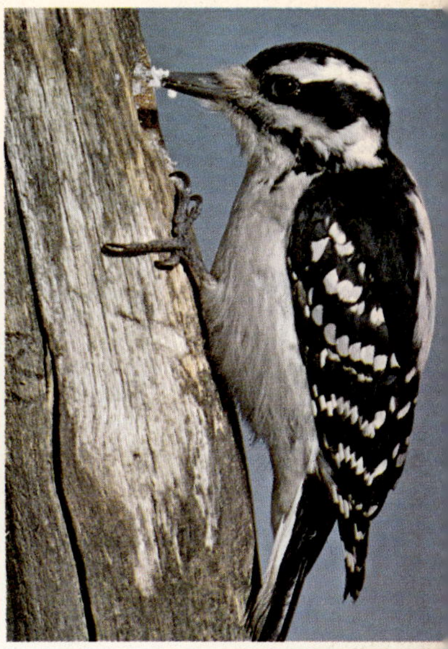

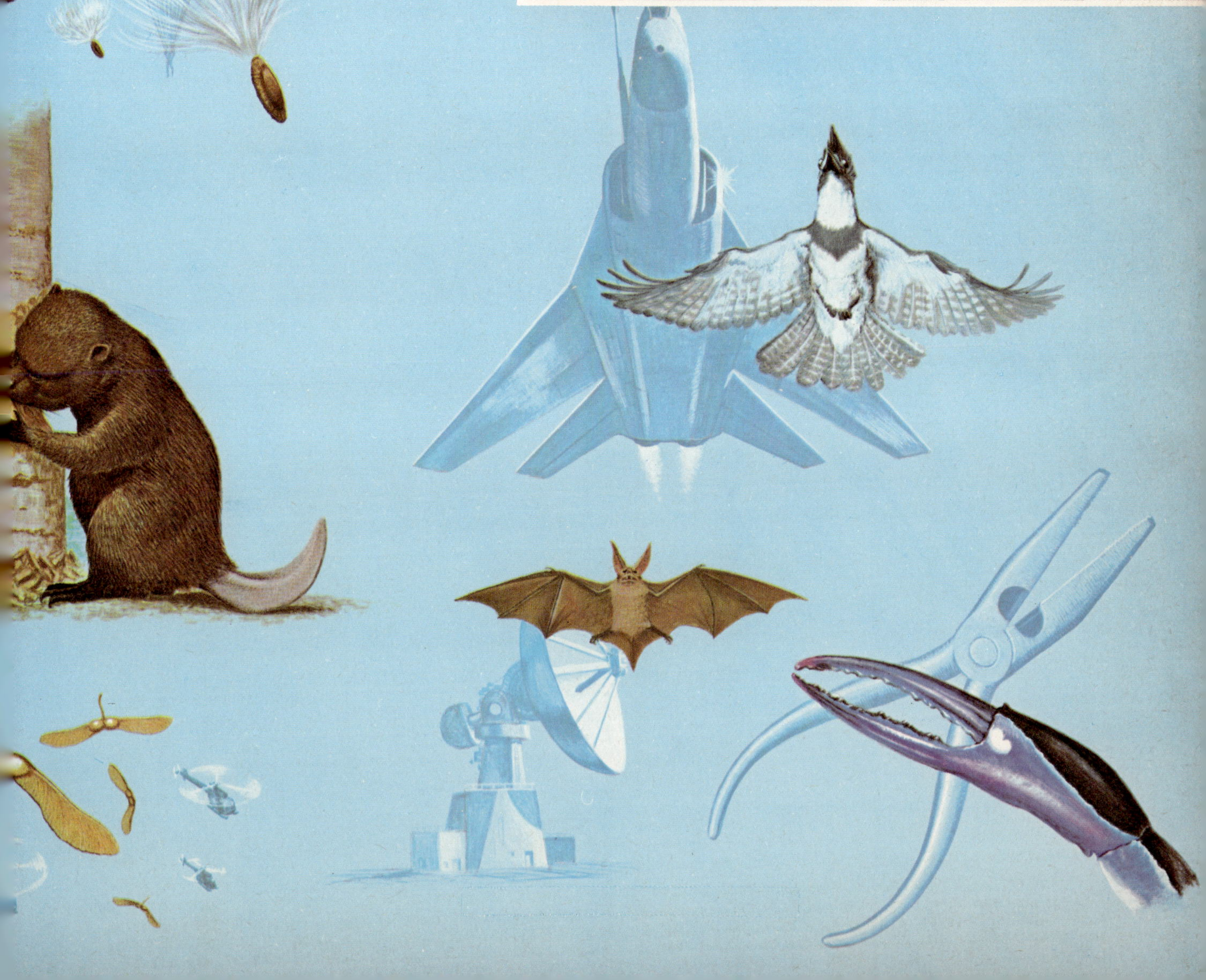

170 / ANIMAL WORLD

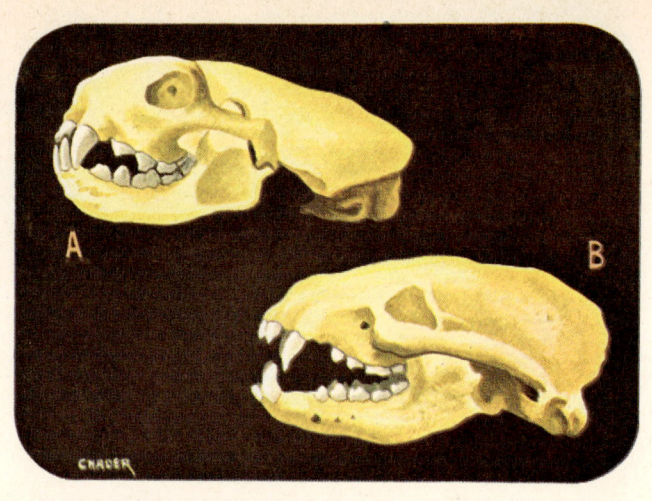

(top left)
A **downy woodpecker** bores in wood to feed on insect grubs. Delicate bones absorb the force of the chisel-beak as it is hammered into the wood, but it is not entirely clear to us how the woodpecker avoids shock to its brain.

(top right)
As we can see from their skulls, the **jaws** of the polecat (A) and badger (B) have a peculiar shape which makes them especially effective as **clamps**. The lower jaw hinges on the upper jaw and they lock in such a way that the mouth cannot be pried open without breaking a jaw.

In human terms, a whirligig beetle is a combined aeronaut, parachutist, surface craft and skin diver. The time may yet arrive when man may perfect a vehicle that enables him to pursue these four methods of locomotion with only minor adjustments; if so, the necessary inventions to make such evolutions possible are likely to be evolved without reference to the whirligig beetle, because this would be consistent with the previous history of human inventions.

Nearly everything man has invented mirrors something in the animal world, yet until quite recent times his inventions had been arrived at independently, or almost wholly independently, of their natural counterparts. Only within the past few decades has this been appreciated, with the result that there is now a greater tendency to look to the animal kingdom for ideas, or to improve on human inventions already in existence. Even so, all too often, we cannot fully appreciate the natural invention until something very like it has been invented by man independently.

Apart from one notable exception, which will be discussed later, man has invented little that cannot be found in some form in the animal kingdom. Most things are there, from the humblest household utensils to the complicated apparatus of modern technology. There is sufficient duplication to make this sweeping statement almost true.

Early Human Inventions

HUMAN INVENTION BEGAN with the earliest man to make a tool. How long ago that was it is difficult to say because modern research is continually pushing the date farther back; but if we say it took place 100,000 years ago it will suffice for our present purpose. During these thousand or so centuries many tools, implements and gadgets were evolved, but progress was slow through the Stone Age. It quickened in the Bronze Age, and more so in the Iron Age. With the advent of the Industrial Revolution progress was suddenly speeded up, and there has

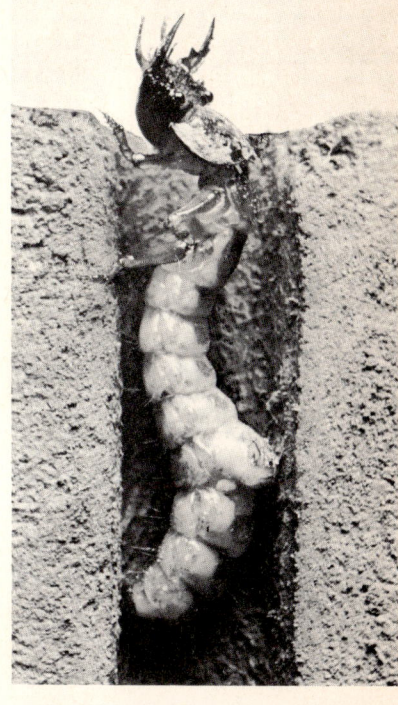

(above)
The **tiger beetle larva** digs an elevator-like shaft and camouflages the opening with its flattened head and prothorax (the first segment in back of the head). Here it lies in wait for its prey, which it will seize with the long, pointed fangs on top of its head and drag down into its burrow to eat.

(above)
This Macrodontia *cervicornis* beetle from Central and South America, with its colorful brown and black markings, has an impressive pair of **pincers.** Such a tool, which resembles a pair of pliers, would certainly be useful for grasping.

(right)
Two knife blades working against each other form a pair of **scissors,** an excellent model for which is the claw of a **crab.** There are some crabs that cut "caps" of sponge, which they use to camouflage their shells; when deprived of their sponge-cap they have been known to cut a circle out of paper.

172 / ANIMAL WORLD

(right)
This is the **skeleton** of that master-tunneler, the **mole,** which excavates a labyrinth of underground passages. The long head and body make burrowing easier, but the most specialized tool of this animal is the front paw, which combines a fork and a spade—or a series of picks and a shovel. Note too the sharp teeth, used for crushing the shells of insects.

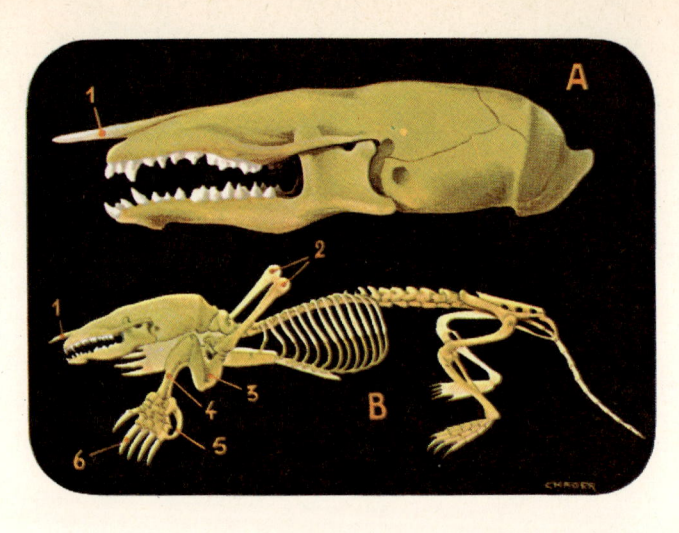

(above)
The **pick-and-shovel** front paws of a **mole** enable it to dig in hard earth, while its wedge-shaped head gives it a further advantage.

been a marked acceleration during the last half-century, with a spectacular proliferation of inventions far outstripping anything previously known.

In comparing human inventions with "natural inventions" a satisfactory method is to make an arbitrary distinction as between those human inventions in existence prior to the Industrial Revolution and those that arose later. More briefly, we can refer to them as the simpler and the more complicated inventions.

When comparing human inventions and animal structures a degree of latitude must sometimes be allowed. The knife and fork serve to illustrate this well. A knife is no more than a blade with a cutting edge, whether it be the cutting edge sometimes added to that abomination the knuckle-duster (sometimes known as brass knuckles), or a table knife or a razor blade, or even the edge on a flint axe. The cutting edge is commonplace in the animal kingdom, in the mandibles of insects, crabs and lobsters as well as in teeth, particularly those molars of the flesh-eaters such as cats and dogs to which the name "carnassials" has been given. These are the sharp-edged teeth used in shearing or slicing flesh.

We can take this further by comparing these insect mandibles and the flesh-eating mammals' carnassials with scissors. A pair of scissors is no more than two knife blades working one against the other. A purer form of scissors action can be seen in a crab's claws, especially those crabs that cut themselves "caps" of sponge to place over their shells as camouflage. Sponge-crabs, as they are called, have been known to cut out a circle of paper with their claws when deprived of their sponge-cap. The leaf-cutting bee and the parasol ant similarly cut out pieces of leaves; but they do so with their mandibles.

The guillotine—especially that used for trimming paper rather than for executions—works on the same principle as the jaws of the carnivore, and so does any contraption used in a factory for exerting pressure on a cutting edge.

INVENTIONS IN NATURE / 173

A pair of jaws, moreover, can be used for crushing, as when a hyena crunches even the long bones of a giraffe; or as a clamp, as when a badger takes hold and its jaws lock, due to their peculiar shape where the lower jaw hinges on the upper jaw. A badger's jaws lock in such a way that its mouth cannot be pried open without breaking the jaw.

When, therefore, we speak of a cutting edge we range over a number of implements, from knives to scissors, razors to knuckle-dusters, wire-cutters to guillotines, a variety of implements as diverse as animal claws, mandibles and jaws. And although the two sets of "tools" may not appear to be identical they all work on the same principle. This is the sort of latitude we must allow in comparing animal and human inventions. Moreover, the knife merges into the scissors, on the one hand, and into any gripping type of implement, on the other.

While some animals use the counterpart of a knife, or knives, for their meals, it is hard to recall one that uses anything resembling a fork, unless it be the lemur known as the aye-aye, which has comblike

(above)
The **remora,** or sharksucker, "hitchhikes" by attaching itself to another fish, most often a shark. Suction is created by the many grooves in the disk, a modified fin which is located on top of the remora's head.

(left)
Any animal that burrows or scratches the earth with its claw is using a tool that is very much like a **hayfork** or garden fork—and there is no greater burrower than the **prairie dog.** Prairie dogs commonly live in very large colonies, or underground towns, which may extend for miles in all directions.

edges to its front teeth, or rodents that bite a hole in a nut and use the lower incisors to extract the kernel. Nevertheless, if we think of the garden fork or the hay-fork as embodying the same principle, then again we can say that the use of the fork is widespread in the animal kingdom. Every animal that burrows or scratches the earth with its claws is using the equivalent of a garden fork. A mole is even better equipped since its front paws combine a fork and a spade. We may carry this further by describing a mole's front paw as combining a series of picks and a shovel, since it will burrow into ground hard enough to defy a garden fork and requiring a pick to break. Or we could liken the paw of a mole to a hoe, and this would be especially true of the marsupial mole of Australia, with one of its claws very much larger than the others and much more flattened. Indeed for the hoe principle we need go no farther than our own fingernails.

Diverse as these various implements are, their efficiency has a common root. Charles E. Mohr has pointed out that one of man's earliest discoveries was that heavy objects could be raised more easily along a sloping surface than by being lifted vertically. This is the principle of the wedge. It is closely related to the principle of the lever. But where man discovered these two, adapted, modified and exploited them in a wide variety of ways, animals have them built in and cannot improve on them.

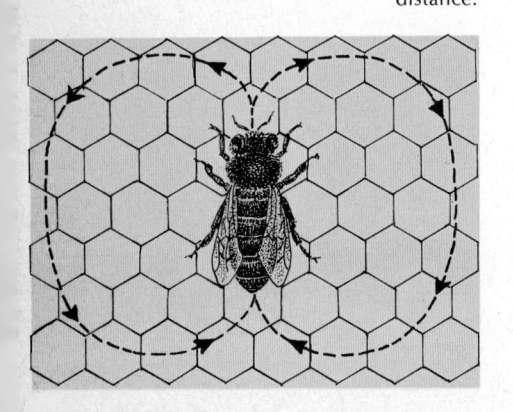

It would therefore be a figure of speech to talk of inventions of Nature but for one thing: that these have arisen accidentally in plants and animals and have been refined by the pressure of natural selection. Similarly in man's development these inventions have almost invariably been discovered accidentally and have been refined by man's ingenuity, often under economic pressure. From this emerges one of the main differences between pre-Industrial Revolution and Industrial Revolution inventions. The first were discovered almost wholly by accident; the second often were discovered accidentally. But there was more pressure from the demands of increasing mechanization for men to search for inventions, and to improve on them. Had we the time to go into it here we should find that accident has been tremendously important in the history of human discoveries.

Honeybees have an amazing system of communication. The "round dance" (below) reports a nectar source close to the hive, while the "figure-eight dance" (bottom drawing) indicates a distant source, its direction and distance.

Why Similarities Exist

ONLY ONE OTHER THING need be said at this point: that the simpler pre-Industrial Revolution inventions bear so close a resemblance to "natural inventions" largely because they represent the only possible way of achieving a particular end. The beaver builds a dam the way it does because there is no other way of building an efficient dam with those particular materials, and men building a dam with the same materials must necessarily build the same way as a beaver does. If man wants to make a pair of bellows he cannot avoid constructing them

(left)
A **beaver dam** is an astounding construction, demonstrating careful attention to the depth of the water and the character of the stream bottom as well as remarkably coordinated work. Some of these structures are of monumental size. Yet, considering the materials it uses, a beaver has no other choice than to build in this manner.

(above)
A **spider's web** is a silken snare that is strong enough to hold a struggling grasshopper. Spiders have had their spinning equipment since long before man developed his own. Moreover, their methods are similar not to our earliest efforts but to our most modern ones, those by which synthetic filaments are manufactured.

like a pair of lungs. A pump must resemble a heart; oars to drive a boat through the water must resemble the legs of a whirligig beetle, because they are doing the same work. It is not surprising therefore that the human inventions should have been started without reference to the natural world.

Whoever made the first corkscrew was almost surely unaware that certain seeds are driven into the earth by a corkscrew action. The man who invented the first drill could not have been aware that the long ovipositor of a female ichneumon fly acts as a drill when she lays her eggs in the bodies of grubs tunnelling in wood. In this instance the comparison is very close because the spiral groove which marks the long shaft of the ovipositor leaves room for little doubt about its function. Moreover, while in action, the drill is braced by two long supports, structures accessory to the ovipositor, as well as by the insect's six legs, these taking the place of the supports that keep our drills straight.

Stitching and Fastening

INSECTS SUPPLY a high percentage of the parallels with human inventions, largely because there are so many different species—upwards of a million. Even so, some of them are surprising. When man began to clothe himself he needed fastenings for his garments. The straight pin must have come first, but this was later followed by the brooch fastening or safety pin and the hook-and-eye, all of which have to a large extent been superseded by the modern "zipper" type of fastener.

One of the main differences between moths and butterflies is that the majority of moths have a means of fastening the fore-wing and the hind-wing together in flight. Male and female moths use slightly different devices to this end, but in both these resemble closely either the hook-and-eye or the safety pin. In the male the fastening has reached a more refined stage and fulfils more completely the function of a safety pin. A spine on the hind-wing fits into a straplike catch on the fore-wing and when so engaged looks remarkably like a safety pin and is just as efficient.

In honeybees we have virtually a zip-fastener on the wings. A row of hooks on the hind-wing engages in a fold on the hind edge of the fore-wing, when the bee is flying. This ensures that the two wings act as one, adding power and speed to the flight. On landing the two wings can be disengaged. This device is as effective as a zip-fastener and it is more efficient. Certainly it less often goes wrong.

The vane of a bird's wing is made up of barbs and barbules which engage each other by hooks. When a vane has become disarranged and dishevelled the bird runs its beak along it and the smooth surface is restored, by what is essentially a series of sophisticated zip-fasteners, similar to those now used in our clothing.

Whether Eve really did spin while Adam delved, as the old doggerel has it, is something that never can be proven, but spinning is certainly a very ancient human activity. It seems almost banal to mention

(above)
The female **ichneumon fly** uses her **ovipositor** (a long tube through which her eggs are laid) to bore into wood in which grubs have tunneled. Her eggs are deposited in the body of a grub and the larvae feed on their host. Like man-made **drills**, the shaft of the ovipositor is marked by a spiral groove.

(below)
A female **grasshopper** lays a series of cigar-shaped eggs in the ground. This is done through the ovipositor, or egg-laying organ, at the tip of her abdomen. The shaft of the ovipositor has the form of a wedge with saw-tooth edges for **drilling**.

that spiders had their built-in spinning equipment at an even earlier date. Moreover, the method by which spiders' silk is produced by-passed the clumsy use of the spinning wheel and yarn and resembles more closely that discovered in more recent years, by which nylon and other synthetic filaments are manufactured.

There is nothing to compare precisely with the eyed needle, as such, but sewing has been used in Nature. The tailor-bird makes its nest in a pouch formed when the bird sews the edges of leaves together. It does this using grass strands inserted through holes pierced by the bill, the strands then being knotted to make them hold.

Perhaps the most spectacular animal accomplishment in this field is in the way certain ants stitch leaves together. The ants are species of *Oecophylla*. Several ants pull the edges of two leaves together by standing on one edge and reaching forward to grasp the other edge with their jaws. Should the gap be too wide to allow the ants to reach across they will form living chains, each ant in the chain gripping the one behind with its hind legs. When the edges of the leaves have been drawn together other ants join in, each carrying one of the colony's grubs held between its jaws. The grubs, which emit silk from the lower lip, are passed back and forth like shuttles until the two edges of the leaves are firmly held together by silk and the gap between them closed with a solid sheet of silk. A damaged nest can be repaired in the same way.

Nor was Adam the first to dig. Indeed, the surprising thing is not so much the number of animals that excavate the soil, either to find food

An Indian **tailor-bird** sews the edges of leaves together to form a pouch for its nest. It uses grass fibers as thread and knots them to make them hold.

When **weaving ants** mend a tear in their nest, they first pull the torn edges together and then use their larvae as shuttles for threading silk across the gap. Each ant carries one of the larvae, or grubs, in its jaws, and the larvae give off silk from a gland in the lower lip.

178 / ANIMAL WORLD

(right)
Flipping open the lid, a **trapdoor spider** springs out of its underground tube. The camouflaged, circular lid is **hinged** with silk and designed to fit the opening exactly.

(far right)
Wasps chew fragments of wood that they scrape from posts or dead tree trunks. Their saliva converts the wood to **paper,** which they use to make their nests.

or make a shelter, but the variety of ways in which they set about doing it. It may even be that more efficient methods could be invented by man should he make an intensive study of the ways in which animals bore through the earth.

Some of the astounding feats in human engineering include the cutting of tunnels through mountains, and here the most spectacular achievement lies in the way one group of workers starts excavating on one side of the mountain and another starts from the other side, to meet exactly at a calculated position far underground. This calls for skill in mathematics and the use of precision instruments. A blind mole, working underground and boring a new tunnel, will make it connect precisely with a pre-existing tunnel several feet away. How it manages this nobody knows, but there is a clear comparison to be made here between animal and human capabilities.

Wasps were making paper to construct their nests long before man

(left)
Ornamental gardens and other outside **decorations** are not solely the inventions of man. Male **bowerbirds** decorate their bowers with flowers, shells, bright objects and leaves. Some lay out a lawn ornamented with flowers and enclose it with a kind of fence, and some even **"paint"** the bower walls with berry juices.

Leaf-cutter ants chew up pieces of leaves to make a compost on which they **cultivate** an edible fungus. The resulting "mushroom bed" supplies these ants with their food.

(above, left)
Since the **water spider** needs air to breathe, it weaves a thimble-shaped **"diving bell"** of silk. This is filled with bubbles of air which the spider brings down from the surface, trapped in the hairs that cover its body.

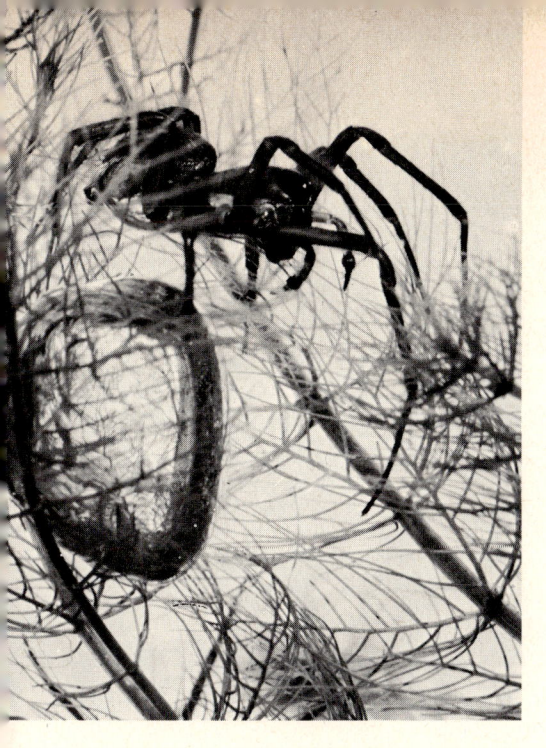

even appeared on the earth. Thrushes have been using stones as anvils on which to crack the shells of snails. The gizzard of a bird is a mill used to crush grain before it enters the stomach for digestion. Water spiders use a diving bell, an inverted thimble of silk in which air can be stored. The archer fish uses drops of water ejected at high velocity and astonishing precision to shoot down insects flying above the surface. One species of spider makes a silk thread with a ball of silk at one end which it throws at an insect flying by, in a fair resemblance to a bolas. This is merely a further random sample of parallels between animal and human inventions.

Animals Practice Husbandry

HUMAN CIVILIZATION was set firmly on the road to further progress when man gave up hunting for husbandry. When a squirrel buries nuts and fails to return to some of them, these germinate and new trees and shrubs result. There are many examples of this form of accidental husbandry among animals, but there are a few instances in which it is more deliberate. The most familiar example is found in the leaf-cutter ants. The workers go out and each cuts a portion of leaf which it carries back, held in its jaws, the piece of leaf held over the ant's head. This has given rise to the alternative name of parasol ant, because it was first thought to be shielding itself from the sun. Back in the nest the leaf fragments are chewed and placed in special chambers. The ants' feces are added, and on the resulting compost a fungus is cultivated. The ants feed exclusively on the fruiting bodies of the fungus. Moreover, when a queen ant leaves the colony for her mar-

180 / ANIMAL WORLD

(right)
In general construction and operation, a **fish's eye** is very similar to a **camera** without a shutter. The lens and diaphragm system is almost identical in function.

VITREOUS HUMOR
CORNEA
LENS
RETINA
OPTIC NERVE
IRIS

(above)
The **principle of the camera** is also demonstrated by the **eyes of an owl**. Note that the automatic diaphragm, or iris, works independently in each eye, so that one eye (or rather, one pupil) may be opened wider than the other, as this picture illustrates.

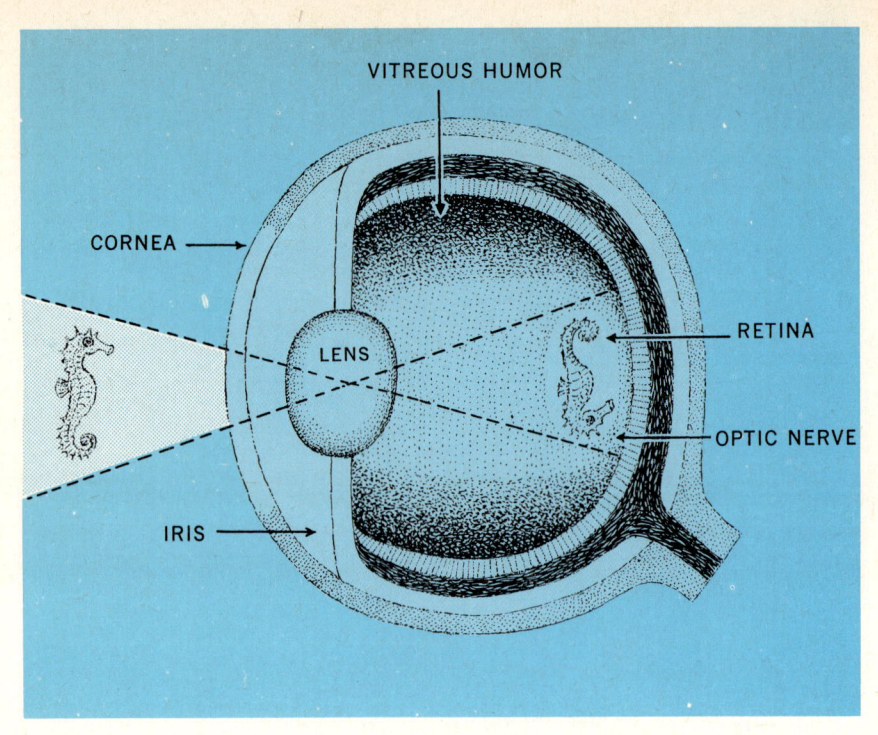

riage flight she carries a pellet of compost containing some of the fungus in a pocket under her mouth. As soon as she has established the site of a new colony she expels the pellet and a new "mushroom bed" comes into being. Although the fungus is a mildew, this is about as close to human mushroom-growing as it is possible to conceive.

Some species of termites, too, cultivate mushroom beds within their colonies, if for mushroom we again read fungus; but with them the purpose is slightly different. Termites feed on any vegetable matter, including wood which they are unable to digest for themselves. The fungus acts on the wood, and "pre-digests" it so that it becomes a useful food for the termites. They anticipated man in the use of artificial or pre-digested foods.

Gardening of a slightly different form is carried out by the giant clam of the Indian Ocean. This clam may grow to be several feet across. Within its tissues live hosts of single-celled green plants which form part of the clam's sustenance. The clam lives in shallow water, where it opens its shell to expose its skin to the sun's rays filtering through the water, and these enable the plants to manufacture the usual sugars and starch. As if to hasten the growth and multiplication of the plant cells, there are scattered in the skin of the clam transparent lenslike structures that focus the sun's rays on the plants. This intensive cultivation anticipated cloche gardening, in which a bell jar is used to protect a plant.

The activities of certain bowerbirds of Australia and New Guinea cannot be described as husbandry but they do parallel closely what has long been a human passion, the cultivation of ornamental gardens. Bowerbirds are famous for the way the male builds a platform of sticks, implants into this a double row of vertical sticks, then displays to the hen as he runs between the two palisades. To carry the story further, the male bowerbird decorates his bower with flowers, shells, bones, bright objects or leaves.

Other bowerbirds have even more elaborate building traditions. They build a tower of sticks around the stem of a sapling, and in front of this lay out a lawn decorated with flowers. They even place a layer of sticks around the garden, forming a kind of hedge or fence, so that the final effect is not dissimilar to the gardens we strive to create around our own houses.

More pertinent to our theme is that some male bowerbirds "paint" the walls of their bowers, using the bright dyes of juices from berries to do so. A few go so far as to make a brush for applying the "paint", by fraying the end of a stick to form a tuft that effectively takes the place of the hairs of a brush.

The discussion about the bowers may appear to have taken us from the central theme of inventions, but it has its place here. Some years ago there was, for a time, a journalistic vogue for showing how feminine fashions often closely resemble the adornments seen in the plumage of birds. Indeed, if one walks down the bird gallery of a large museum with this in mind, or takes a walk through a zoo, it is quite astonishing to see how the head-feathers and the feathered ruffs of many birds look uncommonly like the hats women sometimes wear or the things they put around their necks or drape over their shoulders.

Since man is one with the rest of the living world, and is subject to the same forces, pressures, even desires and aspirations, then we should expect to see this parallelism. It comes out even more strongly when we compare the Industrial Revolution inventions with the more complicated natural inventions. For example, when man wanted to store a permanent record of events, objects and scenes he invented the camera. In general terms a camera is constructed like an eye, with its lens, focusing gear and sensitive plate. Linked with the eye is a brain that contains the apparatus for memory, an apparatus that is often compared nowadays with a computer.

A **white whale** uses its voice as a **depth-sounder.** Research on whales, dolphins and porpoises has already yielded valuable results in the area of deep-sea exploration, a field in which there is renewed and increasing interest today.

Light and Electricity in Animals

OTHER COMPARISONS in the same field of optics are possible. A simple example is seen in the larvae of fungus gnats, found in caves in Australia and New Zealand. People come from all over the world to visit the Waitomo Caves in New Zealand and the Bundanoon Caves in New South Wales. The attraction is the larvae hanging in clusters from the walls and ceilings of the caves, glowing eerily in the dark. The light that these larvae emit is produced by special light-organs be-

ANIMAL WORLD

(right)
A **firefly** has the secret of making light without giving off heat. **"Living light,"** however, is not confined to the firefly's lantern; it is produced by certain marine animals, the larvae of fungus gnats, and other animals as well.

(opposite page, bottom left)
Glowworms, like fireflies, produce light by an efficient chemical reaction. The females are typically wingless, and their light is a beacon guiding the winged males to them in the breeding season.

hind which are reflectors made up of layers of numerous tiny crystals. They concentrate the light and prevent its being dispersed. Each larva has, therefore, a most effective beam-torch. The anomaly is, as so often it is with plants and animals emitting light, that there seems no obviously useful purpose served.

This last is important in view of what was said previously. It not infrequently happens that a man invents something which is not of immediate use, and is not exploitable until something else happens, either to give added refinement to the invention itself or to create a demand which the invention is able to meet. Many inventions, in fact, never reach the stage of practical application. In no other area of animal products is a similar situation so obvious as in the field of living light, such as the fungus gnats emit. For example, a number of marine animals produce light but lack any form of eye or light receptor, or any other means of using the light. The most useless natural luminosity would seem to be the light given out by a certain fungus growing in hollow trees that glows at night.

One should, however, make such statements, about the uselessness of this or that animal structure, with diffidence because often processes and structures found in Nature appear useless or purposeless only until some advance in technology enables us to understand more about them. There is, for example, a fish belonging to the type known as a ray. That is, it is related to sharks but has the flattened body of a skate. In both rays and skates the pectoral fins have become much enlarged and broadened, and associated with them is a large mass of muscular tissue. In the electric ray, known as *torpedo*, these muscle masses are modified to form electric cells, capable of generating 220 volts—greater than the pressure at which domestic current is supplied in most countries. Although we have no written record of what people thought who caught an electric ray, in the days before electricity was understood, we can guess at their bewilderment. We can also imagine their greater perplexity when they saw, as sometimes happens, a leopard shark leaping into the air, with spasms of terror and discomfort, as a ray sent out its violent shock waves. This may be one reason why the ancient Egyptians immortalized the electric catfish of the Nile by depicting it on their monuments. Before men could understand these things the first electric cell had to be invented. Even so, the Arabs used this fish in the treatment of epilepsy as far back as the eleventh century.

However, we can take this story further. In due course, radar was invented. The discovery of radar was in itself a supreme example of the accidental nature of human invention. With the understanding of this process and the invention of instruments necessary to test it, we realized that, in addition to killing prey and repelling enemies, an electric ray uses its electricity to transmit micro-voltage waves similar to underwater radar. These enable the fish to avoid obstacles, and possibly to communicate with other rays.

Bats and Echo-location

THE ACCIDENTS LEADING to human knowledge of animal inventions cannot be better illustrated than by tracing the history of discovery of bats' echo-location. In 1793 Lazzaro Spallanzani, an Italian scientist, became interested in the manner in which animals were able to find

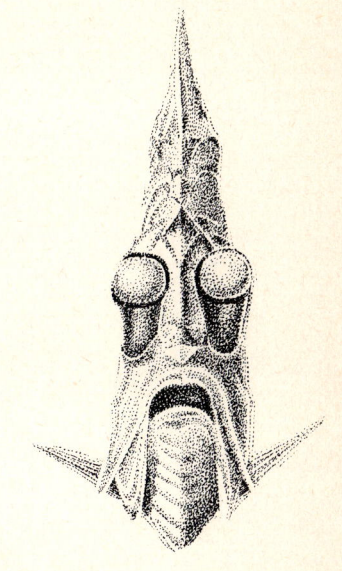

(above and below)
So little is known of life in the deepest oceans that scientists do not really understand why some fish, such as the **silver hatchet fish,** are **luminescent.** The light they produce may attract the small animal life they feed upon.

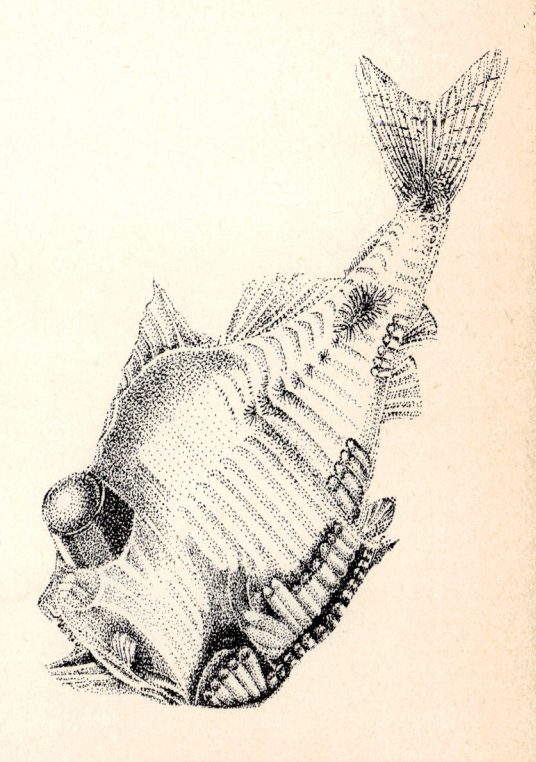

LATERAL LINE WITH OPENINGS

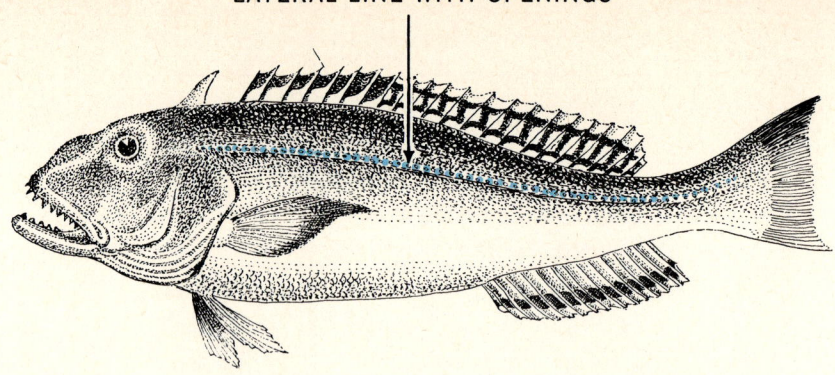

(right)
The **lateral line** of a fish is used to detect changes in pressure and currents in the water. Without it, the fish could not avoid bumping into things, sense the approach of an unseen enemy or find food at night.

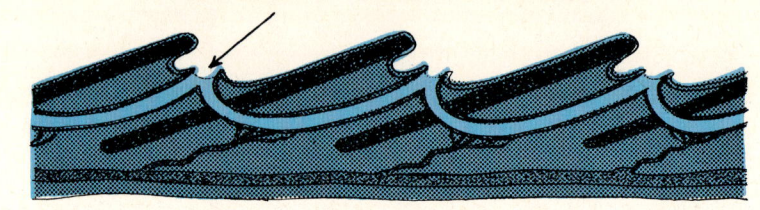

OPENINGS OF LATERAL LINE CANAL

CROSS SECTION

In normal position (below, right), as it might be found in the soil, under a rock or board, the **sowbug** resembles a miniature armadillo. When threatened, its defensive position (below) is the same as that of the larger animal: it curls up into a ball. The overlapping plates are a good protection against small predators.

their way in the dark. He performed what we today would regard as horrible experiments. He caught some bats in a bell tower, put out their eyes and then let them go. Some days later he returned to the tower, caught the same bats, killed them and found their stomachs filled with insects. So clearly, although blinded, they were still able to pursue and catch flying insects.

Other experiments convinced Spallanzani that part of a bat's ability to catch insects in total darkness depended on its hearing. However, as bats appeared to be silent, his theories were ridiculed.

In 1926 Professor Hartridge, at Cambridge, England, noticed bats flying from one room to another of his laboratory while he was working late in the evening. The door between the rooms was nearly shut; yet the bats passed through the narrow slit without brushing

INVENTIONS IN NATURE / 185

(above)
The **lesser horseshoe bat,** shown here in flight, uses **echo-location** to pursue insects and to avoid obstacles in the dark. The horseshoe is a device by which the bat "beams" a solid object in its path.

(above)
A **porpoise** uses echo-location to detect obstacles and to test the depth of the water. Like radar, depth-sounding, or **sonar,** is both an invention of nature and one that man has developed and applied for his own purposes.

the sides, and they continued to do so even after he switched off the lights. Hartridge concluded that bats were able to avoid obstacles in the dark by hearing, and he suspected they were using the voice. He did not pursue this study, and so it remained only an untested idea.

Even before this the American G. W. Pierce had invented and developed an electronic device for detecting sounds outside the range of human hearing; but it was not until 1938 that Donald R. Griffin used the apparatus to test a live bat. He found that bats are squeaking all the time they are flying although we cannot hear them. Each squeak they make is reflected back from solid objects in their path as an echo, which tells the bat how far away an object is. This is echo-location, as it came to be called.

As early as 1912 a device was invented to use echo-location for detecting icebergs at sea, and in 1914 one device located an iceberg at two miles' distance from a ship. Before long this listening device was being used to find the depth of water under a ship, and today no ship is without its depth-sounder, known also as sonar. Once Griffin had made his discovery about bats, it was not long before it was discovered that other animals than bats use echo-location of

(above)
Most heavily **armored** of living animals, the **armadillo** is otherwise without protection. Its armor, therefore, serves much the same purpose as a snail's shell—it is merely a refuge.

(above, right)
The hard **shells** of bivalve mollusks are not much protection from predators, some of which bore through them, while others pull them apart, crush them, crack them or even swallow them whole. It is worth noting that the **hinges** displayed by such shells are as varied as the ones invented by man.

some kind, including dolphins and porpoises, which use it as a depth-ranger as well as for detecting obstacles. This discovery and that of radar have opened up a whole new world of biological discovery, and each new human invention in this field uncovers yet another in which animals are using the same device.

In aerial warfare aircraft flying at night are fitted with an apparatus for upsetting the radar on the planes pursuing them. A discovery within the last few years is that certain moths give out sounds to disrupt the echo-location of bats pursuing them.

If the two devastating world wars of this century have taught us nothing else, they have revealed the speed with which inventions multiply under pressure of events threatening people's survival. They also show how weapons of attack and defensive measures leapfrog over each other. The tank, when first used, found the enemy unprepared to deal with it; but it was not long before specialized anti-tank guns were produced. Indeed, there was an incident on the Western Front in France, in 1918, which would have been amusing had it not been so grim. The German army attacked the British line with captured British tanks, which were knocked out with German anti-tank guns captured previously by the British army.

It is commonplace in biology today to speak of the pressure of natural selection. This is analogous to pressure for survival on nations at war. And it produces much the same result. In former times, soldiers wore armor developed from the helmets, breast-plates, shields and metal coverings on arm and shins that the Roman legionaries wore. This gave a great advantage, so much so that armor was more and more elaborated until knights were so heavily clad from head to foot that they were unable to move freely when dressed for battle. At the battle of Agincourt the French knights, weighed down with plate, were defeated by nimble unencumbered English bowmen with their deadly arrows.

Armor had been evolved again and again in the animal kingdom, the best example being the armadillo, which looks as nearly like a tank as any animal could. But this heavy plate does not make the animal invulnerable. Tortoises and turtles are heavily armored and, until man began to interfere with them, had survived in good numbers, but armor is more typical of animals that have become extinct than of those that have survived, as our fossil record shows.

There is also a whole group of lower animals which have specialized in armor, either as a spiral shell, or as a bivalve shell, like that of the oyster and clam, and all these have numerous predators. These species survive more because of their high rate of reproduction than because of the immunity conferred by a hard shell. There are predators that bore through their shells, or pull the shells open in the

Beetles often have the appearance of **heavily-armored** animals. This is mainly due to their hard, protective **elytra,** which are forewings modified to a pair of thick coverings that meet down the middle of the back, but there may be additional protective covering as well. Interestingly, the fossil record shows that armor is more typical of animals that have become extinct than of those that have survived.

188 / ANIMAL WORLD

case of bivalves, crush them or crack them—or even swallow the mollusk whole and allow the digestive juices to dissolve the shell.

Incidentally, within the range of bivalve mollusks there is a wide diversity of efficient hinges to equal the wide range of hinges man has devised. And if we look to the plant kingdom there are others, in insect-eating plants such as the Venus' flytrap.

Warlike Developments in Animals

Pursuing the theme of animal inventions that recall man's ingenuity in warlike machines and devices, there are four types which deserve further comment: the snorkel, the flying machine, artillery and chemical warfare.

The first submarine was a clumsy affair but early in the history of underwater craft the principle was recognized that survival depended on two things: seeing without being seen, and having some means of renewing the air in the submarine. These two requirements are fulfilled in many aquatic animals. A hippopotamus or crocodile has eyes and nostrils set well up on the head, so that the animal may remain wholly submerged except for these organs, which break surface and no more. Thus these animals can both see and breathe without exposing themselves to view. There are fishes with specially adapted eyes, like the "four-eyed fish". This has only the usual two eyes, but each eye is divided into two, the upper part for vision at the surface, the lower part to keep watch at the same time below the surface.

A man-made submarine also needs to replenish its air supply and this was done for years by bringing the craft to the surface, until the pressure of survival came into play. The development of wide-ranging observation planes provoked the invention of the snorkel, which enables the submarine to use "air-breathing engines" while submerged, and to replenish its air supply without surfacing. This also is an example of how little human invention is influenced by the natural models waiting to be copied. Even in the days of ancient Greece men walked on the sea-bed and were able to breathe by holding

(bottom left)
A **snake** has **scales** which resemble the caterpillar track on a tractor. Forward movement is made possible by the pressure of these scales and of the wriggling sides of the snake's body against the rough or uneven ground.

(bottom center)
A hinged **Venus' flytrap** leaf snaps shut, catching an insect inside. The trap is triggered by an electrical impulse that sets off a chain of cell reactions. It is **water power** that brings the two halves of the leaf together.

(bottom right)
The **mudskipper**, a type of fish, spends long periods of time out of water and can even climb trees. It usually feeds when the tide is out, pursuing hopping shrimps and small crabs on the muddy bottom. The eyes, located high on the head, function like **periscopes** and help the mudskipper in searching for its prey.

a long tube to the mouth, its upper end above the surface of the water. And a study of animal inventions would have revealed numerous examples of aquatic animals having long breathing tubes which could be pushed above the surface of the water to take in air.

The most striking of them is the rat-tailed maggot, the larva of a hoverfly, which can live in foul water with the help of a telescopic tail. Without stirring from the bottom of the pool, the rat-tailed maggot can extend its breathing tube up to the surface and beyond in order to take in air. As it lies on the bottom of the pool the tail of the rat-tailed maggot is easy enough to see because it cannot be completely retracted. When the maggot needs to breathe, however, the tail can be pushed out to an astonishing length, and in superficial view it is extended in the same way as we might pull out the sections of a telescope.

One reason why man was so long in hitting upon the same idea would have been that this particular maggot is not especially well known. It is known to naturalists, but naturalists do not design submarines. Even if there had been someone who was both a submarine designer and a naturalist it might not have occurred to him to apply the principle of the natural invention to the man-made machine. This needed the stimulus of a situation in which the lives of submarine crews were in jeopardy from aircraft lurking in the skies. Perhaps even more than this was needed: losses in underwater craft sufficiently heavy to imperil the chances of victory for a whole nation at war.

Under urgent circumstances like these the call goes out to the inventors and designers, who try this, try that, and try the other thing,

(above, left)
A **crocodile** can lie in wait for prey that comes to the water's edge. Surprise is achieved because this reptile can lie fully submerged with eyes and nostrils exposed, seeing and taking in air without being seen.

(above)
As a rule, man is the only animal to use tools regularly, but there are a few exceptions. A **thrush** sometimes uses a stone as an **anvil** on which to crack open snails for food.

until at last someone hits upon a workable idea. Possibly the first idea does not work, nor the second. By trial and error, by trying out and discarding or modifying, in due course the appropriate device reaches the drawing-board stage. From there it goes into the workshop, and finally it must be fitted to a submarine and then rigorously tested.

This illustrates the history of most, if not all, inventions. Without thinking about it one is apt tacitly to assume that an inventor has a bright idea and from then on everything is plain sailing. At its best there is a hard road ahead of an inventor, from the moment he has his flash of inspiration, or accidentally stumbles upon the idea, until that idea becomes a practical and useful reality. At its worst there are months of frustrated efforts along a road littered with discards, and even at the end there may be complete disappointment.

We say that necessity is the mother of invention. This means that there is more searching for ideas in times of emergency. But it also means that more energy is put into the search, and there is a greater urge to continue striving towards a goal even in the face of disappointment or fatigue.

A single example will serve to illustrate this. When Britain was threatened with invasion, in 1940, somebody had an idea for an easily and quickly made flame-thrower for repelling enemy troops during a sea-borne assault on a beach. It was necessary to use an inflammable material that was available in abundant supply—creosote. The machine was designed and built in record time. Then it had to be tested and finally demonstrated.

For the demonstration, high-ranking officers from the army and navy, as well as civilian observers, were assembled, and the devastating powers of the machine were demonstrated. The engineers who had built it and were working it were almost asleep on their feet: they had had no sleep for three days and three nights. Except in moments of crisis, and especially when survival is threatened, nobody works in this way, on an invention or anything else.

In the end the engineers' efforts were wasted because the invasion never came. But this story illustrates what is meant by "necessity". It was a plain, unvarnished case of survival. And for plants and animals we can modify the phrase: "The need to survive is the mother of

The **wings** of birds are as varied as their habits. Some species can change the wing's shape in flight to execute different maneuvers.

STEERING

TAKING OFF

HOVERING

LANDING

(above)
Early attempts by man to imitate the **flight of birds** met with little success, and yet the same basic problems had to be solved in soaring and gliding flight. Even today, the most skilled glider pilots cannot match the swift, instinctive adjustments of birds to shifts in air currents.

(above)
The **wings of a bird in flight** may have one shape when it is rising off the ground (1) and another when it is gliding through the air (2). Likewise, the curvature of the wings when gliding (A) differs from that of powered flight (B).

invention." We recognize the analogy when we say, as writers about evolution often do say: "Nature has tried out many methods to achieve this end." This means there have been discards; and if our fossil record were more complete we would find, for any natural invention, that the evolutionary history of the species possessing it is a long record of failures, trials and errors, and that in bringing the invention to perfection many other species had become extinct.

How Birds Fly

REVERTING TO THE SNORKEL, it was stressed that human inventors might have saved a lot of time had they gone back to Nature; but they failed to do so. There is another field of invention in which this method was tried but with no great success. According to Greek mythology Icarus made wings of wax shaped like those of a bird, and he failed to fly successfully only because he flew too near the sun, which melted the wax and caused Icarus to plunge into the sea. There have probably been many more attempts to fly since the days of the ancient Greeks, but the first known attempt to study the matter scientifically was made by Leonardo da Vinci. Among his drawings there are many designs for heavier-than-air flying machines, all based on the structure of a bird's wing. Although insects and bats also fly they seem to have overlooked in the search for an efficient flying machine. Even had Leonardo managed to analyze the rapid and complex movements involved in the beating of birds' wings, the kind of machine this might have inspired him to design could not have been made with technological resources of his time.

Otto Lilienthal, in the second half of the last century, pursued the same line. One of his earlier but unsuccessful machines made use of moveable wings covered with large goose feathers sewn to tape. In the end he made a number of successful but very short gliding flights by using rigid wings modelled on the shape of a hawk's wing.

The Wright brothers also studied birds' wings but finally settled on a wing with the camber found in the wings of a fast flying bird. Then, as men more and more took to the air the design of their aircraft departed more and more from Nature. The camber persisted for some time. There was also the German plane of the early days of World War I, known as the *Taube,* meaning dove, which had a faint resemblance to the shape of a bird when seen high in the air. But apart from these, the design of aircraft soon departed radically from the natural flying machines, and birds became almost wholly ignored in aeronautical circles.

Then we suddenly woke up with a start to realize how many items in planes, such as slotted wings, were also to be seen in birds and other natural fliers. The natural laws of aerodynamics were compelling human inventors, working along independent paths, to introduce features found in birds' wings. Or perhaps it is more true to say that not until these features had been incorporated in the man-made machines was it fully realized that comparable structures were already included in birds' wings.

The helicopter was a later invention than the power-driven plane, but already there were hummingbirds and hoverflies that could hover and also fly backwards, forwards and sideways as well as vertically upwards and downwards. The glider, the unpowered plane that uses air currents to keep aloft, was also a later development. And spectacular feats have been achieved in gliders. But the albatross can fly a thousand miles with hardly a wing-beat, by using the air currents travelling

(bottom left)
A natural **helicopter,** the **hoverfly** can remain suspended in the air by a rotary action of the wings. From this position it can suddenly dart in any direction to take up a new hovering position.

(bottom center)
The **rufous jacamar** is a graceful bird and an excellent flyer. It feeds on insects, catching them on the wing with its long, tapering bill.

(bottom right)
By simply using the air currents, an **albatross** can glide a thousand miles with only an occasional wing-beat. Its long, narrow wings are ingeniously designed for varying the angle of flight, essential for swift reaction to turbulent or changeable winds.

Worker ants are sterile females. Besides doing the work of the colony they combine to defend it, squirting formic acid at intruders from a sting at the hind end of the body.

(below)
When in danger this **bombardier beetle** explosively discharges a liquid chemical at its enemy. This liquid quickly changes to a tiny cloud of ill-smelling, irritating gas.

(below)
Skunks are not always quick to use their special weapon—a squirted liquid that turns into a gas cloud with a strongly disagreeable odor. Often they may become quite tame as well. If annoyed or startled, however, they may release their "poison gas."

up the waves of the oceans. Its gliding abilities exceed by far anything man has so far achieved, but this is because it not only has a built-in glider but also the built-in instinct for split-second manipulation of its wings and tail.

The Use of Artillery

ANIMALS MAY NOT HAVE PRODUCED any spectacular inventions in the field of "artillery", but there are plenty of examples of plants using projectiles to scatter their seeds. We are learning, somewhat late in the day, that the human species is the most aggressive in creation, and that war is virtually a human monopoly. However, even though there has been no heavy pressure on animals to produce aggressive weapons operating over a distance, there are a few examples, some of which are combined with a kind of chemical warfare.

Most ants squirt a disconcerting liquid, usually formic acid, at their enemies. The bombardier beetle, from glands at the rear of its body, can eject a chemical in the face of its pursuer. This produces a series of explosions, with machine gun regularity. The spitting cobra can also strike at a distance and, even more effectively, by ejecting the venom from its fangs with deadly effect into the eyes of an intruder from a distance of two feet, or as an intimidating spray up to a distance of seven feet.

The skunks do the same with the liquid squirted from their anal glands, but the main function of the skunk's exudations is to produce a noxious odor, a sort of gas cloud, a truly repellent form of chemical attack.

There are three other examples of this kind worth recording. The marine iguana of the Galápagos islands squirts water at an intruder and so does the red crab that lives in the same habitat. There is also the so-called horned toad, a lizard living in the deserts of the southwestern United States, which squirts blood from its eyes when alarmed. In these three instances we have not yet discovered what effect this form of protection achieves. It may be nearer the truth to suppose we are in the presence of natural inventions that are in the process of being developed, like the half-finished inventions, or those that have misfired, that clutter up the workshops of human inventors.

Most animals possessing chemical weapons have them of more subtle design, resembling the hypodermic syringe. This is essentially a reservoir of liquid with a slender, needle-sharp nozzle which can pierce the skin of an enemy, and down which poison can be caused to flow by pressure on or in the reservoir. The equivalent of the hypodermic syringe is seen in the stinging cells of sea anemones and jellyfishes, as well as stinging nettles and other plants, in the fangs of poisonous snakes, in the poisonous teeth of cone-shell mollusks of tropical seas, and in the poisonous spines of fishes such as the weever and the stingray. It is seen in the fangs of all spiders, and in the hairs of many noxious caterpillars.

Consideration of the hypodermic weapons of plants and animals brings to light another principle—namely, that the same invention may arise again and again, in the natural world, by different routes. The "hypodermic" of sea anemones and jellyfishes consists of special cells whose sole function is the injection of poison, and each cell has its own trigger that, when touched, either by prey or by an enemy, automatically brings the device into action. The stinging cells of plants and the irritating hairs of caterpillars are closely similar to them except that they have no trigger and work more in the manner of a poison capsule, with one end drawn into a fine tube, the end of which must be broken to allow the poison to flow. But they are hairs or bristles that started with one function and have become modified to perform another function.

For the rest: in cone-shells it is the horny teeth on the tongue, or radula, that form the hypodermics; in snakes it is the true teeth; in weever fishes the spines of the fins; in stingrays it is a large dermal denticle (or skin-tooth) that is the vehicle for the poison; and in

(above)
A **moth's tongue** is a tube which is coiled like a watch spring when not in use. It is like a straw that is flanked on each side by muscle tissue, and in effect it is a form of **suction pump**.

(above)
Most **caterpillars** are unable to defend themselves, but many have hairs on their backs which function like **hypodermic needles,** able to carry an irritating fluid beneath the surface of the skin of anything touching them.

(right)
A **slug** moves on its "foot," a flattened sole along which muscle-generated waves pass. It is an inefficient form of locomotion, but to offset this a slug lays down a **track of slime** to help it move more easily over dusty or uneven ground.

A **sidewinder** throws its body into coils as it rolls along, progressing in a direction at an angle to that in which the head is pointing. While it may seem to move with a wheel-like motion, the wheel is actually an exclusively human invention.

spiders it is the jaws, or mandibles. And in all of these we have structures that started off with one function and have become modified to perform another.

These facts emphasize the random or accidental manner in which natural inventions come into existence. Poison can arise, or come into being, at almost any point in the plant or animal body, as a by-product of the metabolism. In the next stage poison-glands, as special receptacles for the poison, can arise and so localize the by-product. Examples of this are the parotoid poison-glands on the head of a toad, the poison-glands in the skin of the body generally, as in the spotted salamander, or the single glands in each flank, as in certain shrews.

After this, it needs only a hollow or grooved tooth, fin-spine, dermal denticle or other structure to be present near the poison-gland, and to undergo a change, for the way to be set for the fully functional hypodermic to evolve.

The Wheel in Nature

BEARING THESE THINGS in mind, it may seem surprising that in spite of the many animal inventions that have their counterpart in human inventions there is one notable gap. The wheel, which enters so widely into human machines and activities, has no counterpart in Nature. Or perhaps it should be put this way, that only by straining at words can we point to the wheel in Nature.

There are certain small aquatic animals which are called rotifers, or wheel-animalcules. A rotifer bears several lobes around the mouth that are decorated with cilia, or fine protoplasmic hairs. These are constantly whipping in a co-ordinated and rhythmic manner, so that to our eyes there appears to be a rotation. That is, each lobe looks like a wheel going round. For this reason, the early microscopists called these animals wheel-animalcules. But this "wheel" is an optical illusion.

In fact, this kind of movement occurs quite commonly in the lower animals and in the internal tubes of higher animals. But a layer of cilia, passing food to the mouth of a rotifer, or passing mucus along our nasal passages or breathing tubes, is better compared with a conveyor belt than with a wheel.

As to the wheel in Nature, we might also use a quibble and say that when a horse runs or a bird uses its wings in flying there is a circular movement of the hoof or the tip of the wing, and that this is, in effect, a wheel action. We might even see in the way a sidewinder snake throws its body into spirals as it moves something of a wheel action; but this is straining at a gnat! The plain fact is that the wheel is a distinctly human creation. However, since, as we have seen with the hypodermic apparatus, there are so many different ways in which the same animal invention may arise, there must have been plenty of opportunity for the wheel to arise in Nature, and there must be a good reason why it is absent; certainly its total absence is highly significant.

It probably means that the wheel, especially as a means of locomotion, is an inefficient organ. This argument is plausible in view of the development of the caterpillar track, which we now fit to vehicles used for particularly arduous tasks. The main trouble with the wheel, as a locomotory device, is that it demands either rails or a level road to work efficiently.

Before leaving the subject of locomotion something should be said about jet propulsion, which was a much later development in the sphere of aeronautics. As a means of locomotion through water it was developed hundreds of millions of years ago by octopuses and squids, using the water taken in for breathing. When this is ejected through a siphon, half the force used serves to propel the squid through the water. The larva of a dragonfly can also travel by jet propulsion, by squirting water from the rear end of its body.

Here again, we have the familiar pattern. So, far from squids and dragonfly larvae serving as the inspiration of the inventor of the jet engine, it was only after jet aircraft had been flying for some considerable time that zoologists studying squids and octopuses began saying, not without some surprise: "Why, these animals are using jet propulsion."

It was about this time that light was beginning to dawn on the problem of bird migration. In the closing years of the 1940s we had many theories about how birds found their way when travelling thousands of miles on migration, but none of these was satisfactory. Then important experiments began to indicate that birds navigated by the

A **squid** swims backwards, moving by **jet propulsion.** It also squirts ink to form a "smoke screen" that can baffle an enemy and paralyze its sense of smell. This ink is the source of the brown pigment called sepia.

INVENTIONS IN NATURE / 197

sun during the day and by the stars at night. Moreover, later experiments showed they were able to allow for the movements of the heavenly bodies. So we began to say that birds, like ships' captains, navigate by using a sextant and a chronometer, except that these are built into the bird's brain, and operate automatically, or by instinct, as we say, whereas the ship's captain has to get out his instruments and laboriously take his readings. But a ship's captain also has a map. What takes the place of the map in a bird's navigation has yet to be determined. It is a mystery yet to be solved. It is sufficient to say at this point that celestial navigation has now been established for insects, fishes and frogs, although in all of these we are still groping for the final answers.

(below)
When tormented, some **whales** have been known to leap out of the water and throw themselves onto a whaling ship. To protect themselves against extreme pressures and the cold of ocean depths, whales have a thick layer of fat under their skins. Some species also have an oil-filled bladder in the head which apparently helps them to hear.

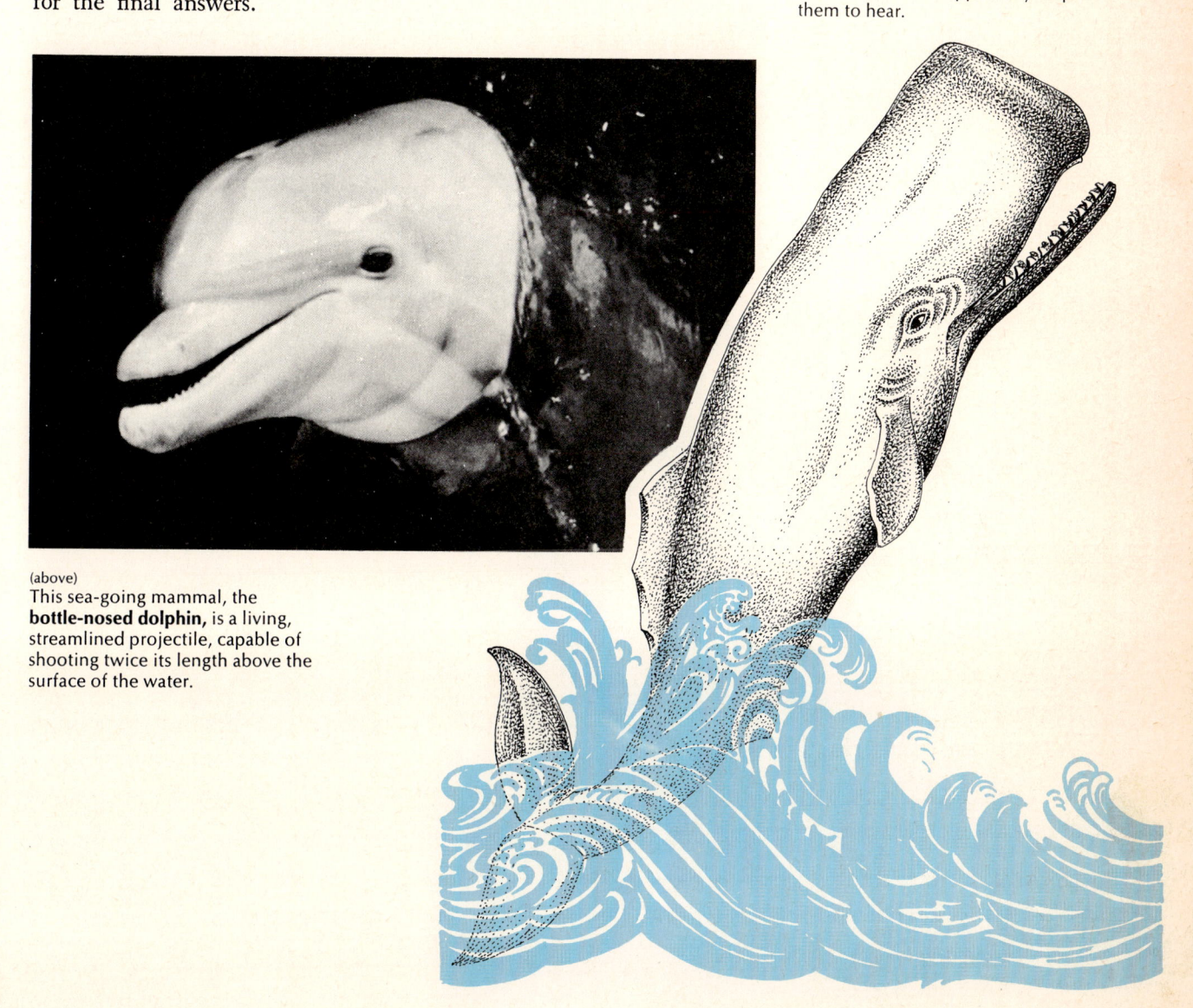

(above)
This sea-going mammal, the **bottle-nosed dolphin,** is a living, streamlined projectile, capable of shooting twice its length above the surface of the water.

(above)
Set high up on its head, the eyes of the **crocodile** function as **periscopes** when the rest of its body is submerged.

(right)
Nature has brought **packaging** to a fine art, showing none of the wastefulness and inefficiency common to modern man. Young animals emerging from their shells always seem too big to have been packaged in such small containers.

Man Looks to Nature

AT THE PRESENT MOMENT all kinds of promising biological research are proceeding in which either an animal invention is helping forward improvements in human technology or human inventions are furthering our understanding of what had previously been animal mysteries. We find, for example, that the pits on the head of the snake known as a pit viper enable it to follow the trail of a mouse by the very small amounts of heat left in the track of the prey. In the laboratory, a radiant heat-detector built on almost the same principle as the snake's pits has been perfected.

For decades we have said of the mallee fowl of Australia that it builds huge mounds of earth and leaves to form an incubator for its eggs and then abandons them to be hatched by the heat generated by the decaying leaves. Now we know the mallee fowl does *not* neglect the mound; it returns periodically during the day and uses its beak as a thermometer to test the temperature. If the temperature has risen above normal the bird opens the nest to cool it. If the temperature has fallen below what it should be more materials are added to raise it. The bird's beak is a thermometer, and the bird's actions are those of a thermostat.

Reference was made earlier in this book to the pre-Industrial Revolution inventions and those of the Industrial Revolution. A third phase can now be recognized as coming into being. We can call it the Age of Technology, but so far as this present discussion is concerned it is not only an age of spectacular advances in invention and discovery but also one in which man is looking more deliberately to Nature for help or inspiration. There is the corollary, that the biologist is being assisted in his understanding of Nature by the inventions made in other fields, often only to discover that the invention he is using is already in existence in some plant or animal.

It would need a vast amount of research to be able to say how far and in what particulars modern technicians and inventors are looking to natural inventions for inspiration and guidance. One example can be cited. A device has now been elaborated which will enable a blind

An insect's **antennae,** such as those on this common **house cricket,** are more delicate and complex than most of those used by us for radio and television reception. Odors, changes in air temperature and humidity, and often other conditions as well can be detected by those of the insect.

(right)
To ensure widespread **dispersal of plant seeds,** nature sends the greatest number traveling with the winds. Some, like the **milkweed,** glide on gossamer parachutes. In the air the seed hangs downward, like a man in a parachute harness.

(above)
The seeds of a **witch hazel** are "fired" several yards when the drying fruits split open with a snap. This is an example of the peaceful use of a projectile.

person to find his way by echo-location. In fact, blind people have long been doing this by tapping a walking-stick on the ground. The new device goes further than this, however. It will enable the blind person to beam on objects, and so to tell more definitively the pattern of his surroundings and especially to recognize the nature of obstacles. This is what bats can do, and it seems only reasonable to suppose that the technicians working on the blind-aid must have profited by the vast research already carried out on the echo-location of bats.

Frank Lloyd Wright built a factory on revolutionary lines in the United States, using thin-stemmed concrete pillars flaring into broad discs at the top. The building proved to be as strong as any other in spite of the delicacy of the pillars. Wright is said to have taken the idea directly from the flowers of the morning-glory plant.

A particular form of dome-shaped building made up of overlapping arched segments is coming into vogue and promises to be more popular in the future. Whether by accident or intention, this method of building resembles closely the fine structure seen in certain bones and shells in which lightness and strength are combined.

It is said that the hull of the submarine *Nautilus* was modelled on the body, and especially the head, of the sperm whale. And recently, when the U. S. Navy needed a lightweight salvage pontoon the engineers took a cantaloupe as a model. The ordinary pontoons with smooth surfaces lacked the tensile strength to stand the stresses involved in rapid inflation and the drop in external pressure as the pontoons rose speedily to the surface.

A cantaloupe has a hollow centre which traps air. The sun warming a cantaloupe heats the air, which expands and exerts a high pressure on the outer skin. It was suspected that the fluted design of the surface of the cantaloupe provided the extra strength. Tests proved this to be a correct supposition and the pontoons were made in the shapes of a cantaloupe, using a rubber-coated nylon fabric. Success was assured.

When the project to land a vehicle on the moon was still in the planning stage, at least one of the proposals for the design of the landing craft drew its inspiration directly from nature. Two of the important considerations facing the scientists were that the vehicle should be as light as possible and that its feet be constructed so that they would not readily sink into any soft rock or other substratum that might be encountered. In addition, if they decided that the vehicle was to move about on the surface, something would have to be done to make certain it did not become bogged down in areas of deep dust, stranding its occupants on the moon. One suggestion put forward, then, was that the vehicle be constructed with four legs and flattened feet and that it be capable of taking leaps like a frog.

Should such a vehicle ever prove practicable, on the moon or elsewhere, we might be some way on the road to realizing a state of affairs resembling the one postulated at the beginning of this chapter. There we spoke of the whirligig beetle enjoying the best of three worlds, in the air, on the water and under the water. A moon vehicle like a frog may seem a far cry from this, but it is worth recalling that the frog's structure also inspired a breakthrough in underwater exploration. The frogman's feet today are a commonplace; but not long ago they were first used with revolutionary effect—for war purposes. They enabled skin divers to go down and quickly deal with underwater obstructions designed to wreck landing craft, as well as to plant time-bombs on enemy installations.

▶ *The many ways in which mammals, birds, fish and even simpler animals move about on land, in the water and in the air.*

Nature in Motion

Anyone can tell a tree from an elephant. One is a plant, the other an animal. If asked to state the most obvious difference between them most people would say that an elephant can move about whereas the tree is permanently fixed. A few plants, however, can move about, and there are some animals, such as corals, that stay in the same place nearly all their lives. Clearly, therefore, we cannot discuss nature in motion without defining what we mean by the word "motion".

All growth involves movement. Even growing crystals sometimes give a vivid impression of movement when seen under high magnification. Within every living cell, also, whether plant or animal, the constituents of the protoplasm are in more or less constant movement. Motion is, however, movement with a difference. Above all, the word implies movement from one place to another, and with rare exceptions this is the monopoly of the animal kingdom.

There are some single-celled plants capable of motion under their own power, because from the body of the cell one or more protoplasmic whips, known as flagella, project, and by their whipping action set up a current in the water that draws the plants along. In fact, these plants

The ever-moving world of nature is full of the whir of wings, swirling dandelion parachutes, hopping kangaroos, sleek fins, racing cheetahs. Although motion is usually thought of as an animal activity, there are plants that move along the ground and animals that stay in one place. Essential for avoiding enemies, finding food, migration, propagation, even just for fun, motion is a basic activity in the living world.

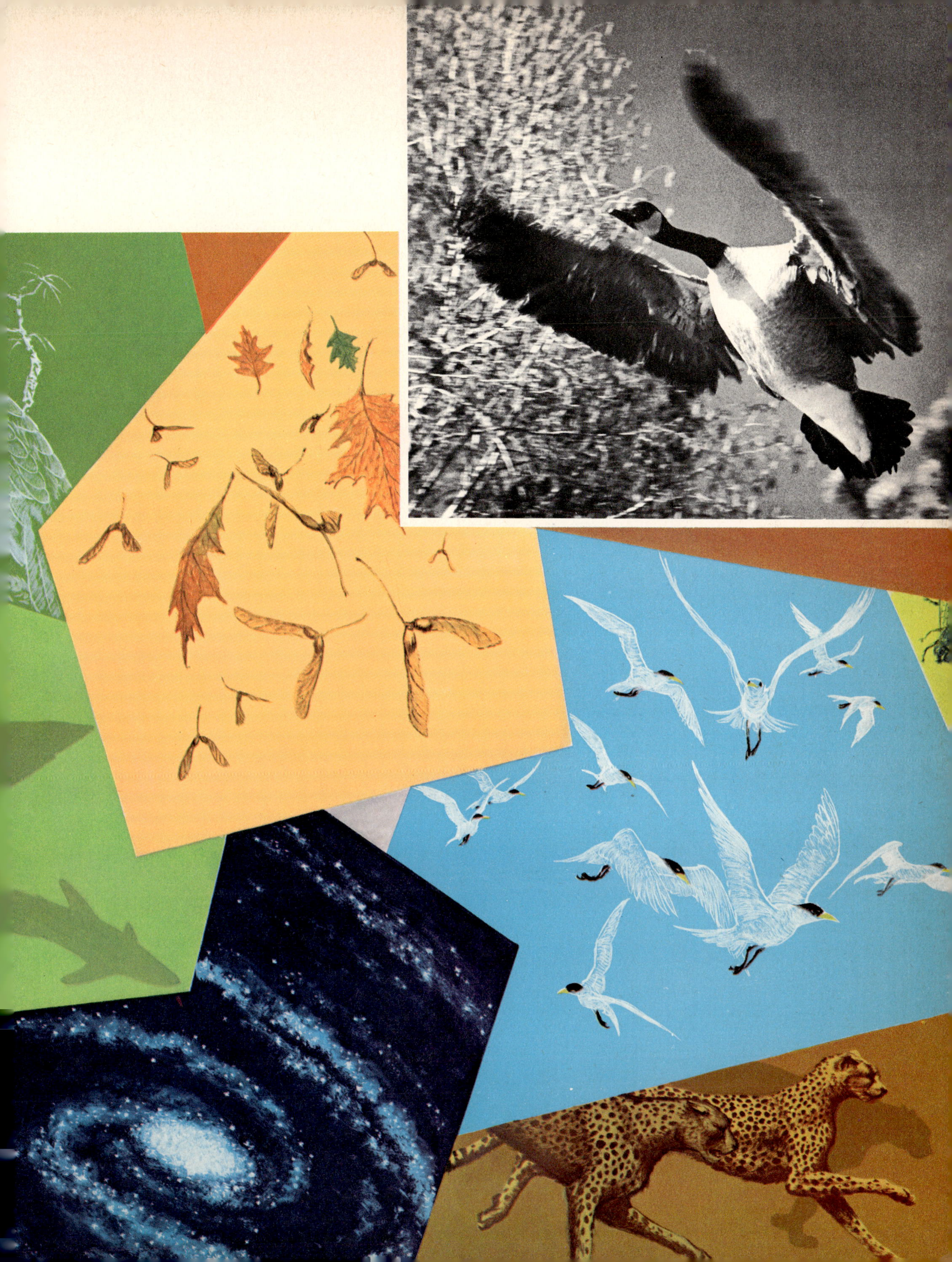

204 / ANIMAL WORLD

(right)
Dandelions owe their widespread distribution to the way their seeds are dispersed. In many plants the seeds drop to the ground and there is competition among seedlings for living space. The majority perish, not being able to obtain the elements necessary for their survival. The dandelion **parachute** (pappus) ensures that the seeds will reach farflung regions, where their chances for light and water will be better.

(above)
Many **seeds** depend on the **wind** for dispersal. Heavy ones, such as these maple seeds, may have wings and spiral down like a helicopter.

swim. There are a few plants which throw out branches that touch the ground, take root and in their turn throw out other branches. Later, the parent plant dies. So these plants do, in a sense, travel over the ground; but they take years to move any great distance. This is not motion as most people understand it; yet it is the best that the plant kingdom can manage, if we exclude certain seeds that are carried by the wind, or by other agencies.

Locomotion has almost the same meaning, except that since it connotes the act of moving from one place to another, it would not apply to movement in space, as when a sea anemone stretches upwards and then retracts itself.

Movement of Simple Animals

THE SIMPLEST ANIMAL exhibiting motion that causes its body to travel from one place to another is the single-celled amoeba. It pushes out a portion of itself and into this false-foot, as it is called, the protoplasm of the rest of the cell flows. By alternately pushing out false-feet and flowing into them the amoeba moves about. The mechanics of amoeboid movement are far more complicated than this would make it appear, but this description is sufficient for our purpose. As an amoeba flows along its action is superficially like that of a drop of oil. In fact, years ago "artificial amoebae" were made by mixing fine sand grains with rancid oil. When droplets of this were placed on a smooth surface they moved about very much as a live amoeba would.

Other single-celled animals are like the simple plants already mentioned. They have one or more flagella, with which they swim. There is another class of single-celled animals that have numerous cilia, or short protoplasmic hairs, covering the body. These are, in effect, short flagella, but there is one very striking difference; cilia show co-ordinated action. They do not move in unison, like oars, but in succession, so that a wave of movement is seen to pass rhythmically through the rows of cilia, an effect that recalls the movement in a field of tall grass as a puff of wind travels over it. The rhythmic action of the cilia causes the animal to rotate, and so to swim.

However, there are some single-celled animals which instead of having numerous cilia have only a dozen or so, most of them on their undersides. Seen under a microscope these animals seem to walk, their cilia behaving like legs.

Among the multi-hued animals the lowest in the scale are the sponges. If there is one member of the animal kingdom that looks like a plant and which seems anchored like a plant to one spot, unable to move, it is a sponge. But appearances are deceptive. This resemblance to a plant is only partial. A sponge starts life as a larva which swims about by means of flagella for many hours before settling on the bottom. Then it changes from an oval larva bearing whiplike flagella to a flattened, transparent platelet of tissue, without flagella, apparently fixed to the surface of a rock. At this stage it looks like a large amoeba, because of its irregular outline.

Groups of sponge larvae settle on one spot, and the platelets into which they change are consequently in a fairly compact group, but with each platelet separated from the next. Then begins a slow dance. For many days after they have settled the young sponges are continually changing their outline. They advance towards each other and then

(bottom left)
Although a **sponge** may look like an undersea plant, its beginnings are actually as free-swimming larvae. Later they attach themselves permanently to a rock, remaining as sedentary as most plants.

(bottom center)
Most of the time the **hydra** is anchored to a pond weed, its only movement being the **stretching** (2) and **retracting** (1) of its body and tentacles. Numbers (3) and (4) illustrate growing hydras, (A) and (B) buds, (C) and (D) stinging cells, (E) an egg and (EF) the internal structure of the hydra.

(below)
Even microscopic, one-celled animals have the means to travel about. The **hairlike cilia** on the body of the **paramecium** act as oars and are used when the animal "swims." This diagram shows a paramecium in cross-section.

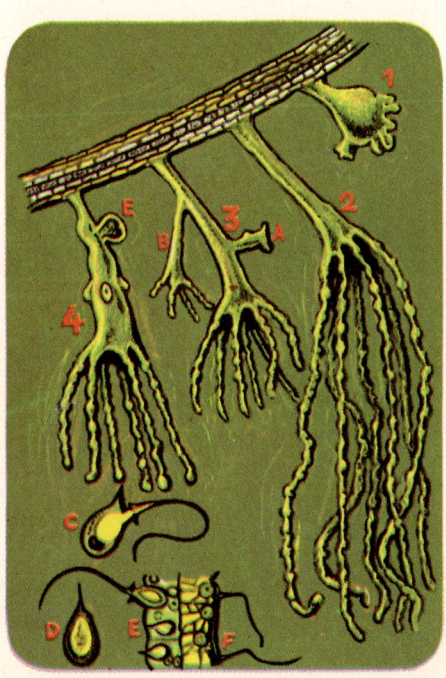

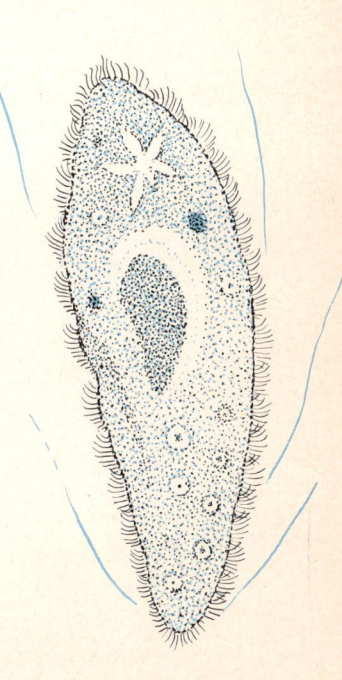

In the Virgin Islands, **elkhorn** or **staghorn coral** grows in prongs like the ones in this photograph, where a branching colony is exposed at low tide.

retreat again, in a kind of ballet; but it is ballet in very slow motion, and one must watch a particular group for hours in order to detect any movement at all.

We can go further: sponges retain this power of movement even when half-grown, and these immature sponges have been observed to move from one place to another, a foot or more away, where food was more abundant. A full-grown sponge tested experimentally also moved—one inch in a week. This is true locomotion, and although so incredibly slow, it sets the sponge apart from the typical plant.

Animals that Look like Plants

OTHER ANIMALS LOW ON THE SCALE are sea anemones and jellyfishes, which are closely related to each other. For the most part a jellyfish only drifts with the current. Yet it can swim to some extent. It can open and shut its bell-shaped body, just as one might open and shut an umbrella, in a pulsating movement by which it can swim upwards or downwards as it is being carried by the current.

Its relative, the sea anemone, seems to be even more fixed. But, again, appearances are deceptive. Like a sponge, the sea anemone begins life as an oval larva which swims about before settling on the seabed and turning into a young sea anemone. Thereafter, its movements are mainly vertical.

NATURE IN MOTION / 207

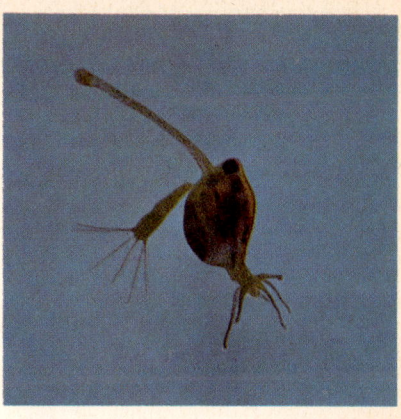

(above)
By a series of **somersaults,** the **hydra** can move from place to place. By stretching and retracting it bends over to grasp with its tentacles, lets go with its foot, then throws the body over to take hold with the foot again.

(above, left)
The slow, pulsing rhythmic motion of a **jellyfish** would seem to be ineffectual, but it is adequate for all of this animal's needs.

A sea anemone's body is columnar, with a mouth at the apex surrounded by a ring of tentacles. Both body and tentacles are capable of extension and retraction. To catch food the anemone stretches up and spreads its tentacles. To rest it withdraws the tentacles and contracts the body, and in the fully withdrawn position it becomes little more than a button of flesh attached to a rock.

This up-and-down motion in a fixed position is not peculiar to the sea anemone, or even to its other relatives the coral animals, sea pens and sea firs. It is also found in the moss animals (known as the Bryozoa or Polyzoa), in many of the tunicates (known as sea squirts) and in a few other more obscure and unfamiliar groups of marine animals. It is almost as if nature has experimented with the vertical motion and found it suitable for certain kinds of life but not good enough for general purposes.

The sea anemones are so called because they look like flowers, and the early naturalists were clearly struck by their plantlike appearance. There is, however, one very great difference between the sea anemone and a plant, and this in turn presents us with another important distinction between plants and animals.

Some years ago it was found, as the result of careful observation and experimentation, that a sea anemone is seldom still; nor are its movements just a matter of stretching up to catch food when hungry and retiring within itself to rest when its hunger is satisfied. The animal is moving all the time in a kind of slow-motion dance. We might almost say it is like a ballet dancer rooted to the spot. It slowly reaches up, spreads its tentacles, sways slightly, pushes out again, withdraws slowly first a few tentacles, and so on, in a wide pattern of movement.

Moreover, the anemone will continue this dance whether there is food present in the surrounding water or not, and whether it is dark or daylight, and even when there is no vibration or stimulus of any kind. The sum total of these movements is called the inherent rhythm of activity; to put it in more homely terms, the animal is born with a built-in impulse to keep always on the move.

This inherent rhythm of activity has been found in all animals so far investigated. It is what makes us go to sleep at night and wake up at dawn, and, what is more, it causes us to move even when asleep. The periods of deep slumber when we are virtually as still as a log do not last long; mostly, while we are asleep, we turn, twist and fidget. This is not because we are uncomfortable. It is due to the impulse to move, the inherent rhythm of activity.

Another fundamental difference between plants and animals is that plants make their own food from carbon dioxide in the air in the presence of sunlight. The air is all around them and the sun's rays come to them. Their feeding is therefore passive. An animal eats food already prepared. It either eats plants or it eats other animals that have fed on plants, so it must go out and get its food, or at least, like the sea anemone, it must make some effort to catch it. Therefore right from the start of its life an animal must be on the move, in some way or other. The ways in which animals move are as varied as their shapes. Indeed, the patterns their movements form are closely related to these shapes.

Before leaving the sea anemones it should be recalled that they, like sponges, will sometimes temporarily give up their sedentary habits and move about horizontally. Collect a score of sea anemones scattered over

(below)
The **turkey vulture** of North America weighs only three pounds, but it has a wingspan of six feet. Like all vultures it is remarkable for its **soaring flight**.

(right)
Albatrosses come to land only to breed. The rest of the time they wander great distances over the oceans, traveling thousands of miles on their spread wings. Only occasionally are the wings seen to beat, the albatross skillfully using the **up-currents** to gain height, then gliding, slowing, losing height, only to use another up-current.

the shore and put them in a rock-pool crowded together. In a few hours they will have moved apart, to spread themselves out. Without such a redistribution the food and oxygen in that one place would soon be exhausted. Motion, and especially locomotion, gives animals as individuals a great advantage in the struggle to survive. When many seeds fall in one place the plants from them must strangle each other to prevent overcrowding; animals can move to prevent overcrowding.

The sea anemones move apart by gliding on their bases. Some anemones habitually do this. Some species even reproduce themselves by gliding over the rocks and leaving behind at intervals bits of their own base, each of which grows into a new separate creature. Some anemones may turn on their sides and pull themselves along by their tentacles. Others will inflate themselves, let go at the base and swim through the water. And there are some species that habitually burrow into mud.

They may only do these things occasionally, but the potentiality for doing so is always there and these excursions foreshadow the methods used by higher animals to get from place to place, to search for food, to escape from enemies, to seek mates, or to explore their surroundings. These are the four main reasons for animal movements. Underlying them all is the inherent rhythm of activity, which compares to a motor ticking over or idling, ready to go when the driver lets in the clutch.

Wave-movement

THE SIMPLEST METHOD of locomotion after that used occasionally by a sea anemone is very like it, except that it is habitual. It is the movement seen in snails and slugs. When a snail comes out of its shell it extrudes a large fleshy portion with a flat underside. We call this its foot because this is the part on which it progresses from one place to another. A wavelike movement of the muscle travels along the sole of the foot that carries a snail slowly over the surface. To make things easier, especially over dusty ground, a gland in the front of the foot constantly exudes slime. A moving snail therefore is always laying down its own track, to make progression easier.

It is easy to study this wave-movement; simply put a snail on a sheet of glass and watch it from below. The movements in the snail's foot recall those used by an earthworm, which pushes the front part of its body forward, then takes hold of the ground. A ripple passes along the worm's body and the hind part is finally drawn forward. By alternately stretching out its front end, gripping, and then pulling in the hind end, the worm moves over the ground or through its burrow. But in an earthworm the motion is made easier by rows of bristles arranged along each side of the body. When the front part of the body is stretched forward the bristles grip the ground, and just before the hind part is brought forward its bristles are lifted.

This is, to state the case simply, because the muscular wave that

(above)
Owls, such as these **saw-whet owls,** have short, round wings and small, square tails. Their plumage is soft and the edges of the flight feathers have filaments that muffle the sound of the beating wings, enabling them to fly in almost complete silence. Only when one is within a few feet of an owl in flight can even the softest sound be heard.

(above)
This **cutlah snake,** with its very large eyes, is nocturnal in its habits. It moves from branch to branch in the tropical rain forest with an exaggerated **looping motion.**

210 / ANIMAL WORLD

(right)
Outside its shell the **snail** moves by means of a muscle that travels along its flat underside and carries it over the surface, somewhat as an earthworm moves.

(below)
The **horse conch** of the Atlantic shores of America, from the Carolinas to Brazil, grows to a length of two feet. It is a giant snail and, like land snails, moves about on a **fleshy foot**.

passes along the worm's body is accompanied by a similar wavelike movement in the bristles. It is, in fact, a short step from this to the movement seen in the legs of a millipede or a centipede, except that in them jointed legs are present. But these legs are not so far removed from the bristles of a worm.

The marine bristle-worms are first cousins to earthworms. In many of them the bristles are mounted on short fleshy stumps, like the beginnings of legs, the bristles then playing the part more of hooks securing a hold than of the actual organs of locomotion, as in the earthworm. This is taken a stage further in a wormlike animal, known as Peripatus, which has a pair of fleshy legs to each segment of the body, with a pair of hooklike bristles at the end of each leg.

Peripatus looks so much like a caterpillar that it is no surprise to learn it is regarded as a forerunner of these insects, linking them with earthworms. In a caterpillar, however, there is not a pair of legs to each segment, or ring, of the body. Instead, there are three pairs of legs on the first three segments behind the head and several pairs of so-called pro-legs at the hind end of the body. The front three pairs of legs of a caterpillar are little better than curved bristles. The pro-legs have a fleshy sole that is used in grasping. A caterpillar advances by holding on with the front legs, then drawing up the hind part of the body and gripping with the pro-legs. The front part of the body is then pushed forward and the process repeated.

In many caterpillars the result is a kind of wave-action passing along the segments of the body, as first the front legs and then the hind legs come into action. In other caterpillars, known as loopers, there is a much wider gap between the front legs and the hind legs, and when the hind legs are brought forward the body is arched into a pronounced loop. Then the body is stretched forward, the front legs take hold again, and the hind legs are brought up to just behind the front legs, again with the body looped.

The action of the looper caterpillars recalls that of a pair of compasses

NATURE IN MOTION / 211

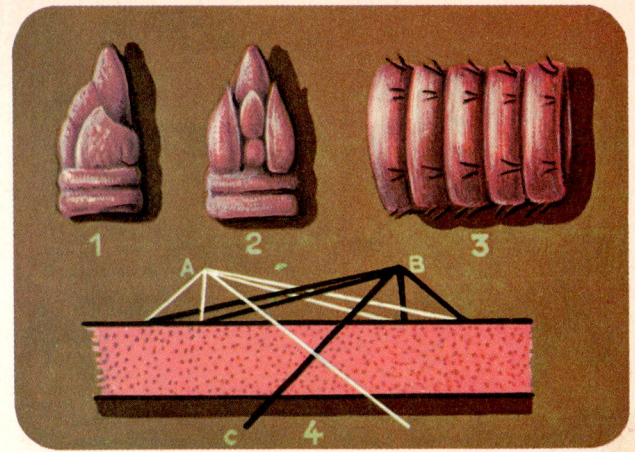

(top, left)
The **rock barnacle** is related to crabs and lobsters. In its larval state it looks very like the larvae of these other crustaceans. Afterwards it becomes a totally different animal, enclosed in a shelly fortress with a movable lid. To feed, it opens the lid and pushes its legs out. These are covered with **bristles,** and when slowly waved in the water, they pick up microscopic plants as in a dragnet.

(top, right)
The movement of an **earthworm** is made easier by **bristles,** arranged in rows (3), which grip first in the front, then in the back, as the worm loops forward. The mechanism of the bristles and the position of the muscles are illustrated in (4). Segments of the head are shown from the side (1) and from the front (2).

(right)
The **millepede** has two pairs of jointed legs on each of its segments, except for those at the end of the animal. It walks with a **wavelike motion,** contracting or extending one group of its legs after another. When disturbed, most millepedes coil into a spiral, while some are able to roll themselves into a ball.

when used on a chart to measure distances. Consequently, these caterpillars are sometimes called earth-measurers, and the family of moths they belong to are called Geometers (or earth-measurers).

The legs of the adult insects into which the caterpillars change are jointed and seemingly unlike anything so far mentioned. Yet if we could lengthen the legs of Peripatus and make their segments hinge on each other we should have something very like the legs of typical adult insects. The idea that the bristles of a creature like an earthworm could evolve into the legs of a beetle or a butterfly seems far from extravagant when the various organs of locomotion are laid side by side. We discover there is a simple and gradual transition from one to the other.

Movement by Wriggling or by Suckers

IN INSECTS ANOTHER KIND OF MOVEMENT is seen, which has nothing to do with legs. On the thorax, which comprises the three segments lying immediately behind the head, outgrowths of the cuticle have become membranous wings. These enable insects to fly. It is best to leave the study of flight until later and to deal with two other methods of locomotion among the lower animals. The first is progression by wriggling or serpentine movements. The second is locomotion by the use of suckers.

Many marine bristle-worms wriggle in order to travel over the seabed, just as snakes do, which is why this kind of movement is called serpentine. Eels swim with the same kind of movement; and the very long slender centipedes often walk with a serpentine movement, as do legless lizards, such as the slow-worm. And this same serpentine movement underlies the swimming movements of the higher aquatic animals, such as fishes, which we shall consider later.

Meanwhile we can discuss the movements of a near relative of the earthworm, the leech. Although it is flattened, and lacks bristles, it has the same ringed body as an earthworm. The usual habitat of the leech

(below, left)
A **leech** usually moves by using two **suckers,** one at each end of the body. It holds with its hind sucker, pushes its front forward and takes hold again. Then it moves the hind one up, takes hold, and repeats the whole motion.

The **sucker** (A) with its three dental **saws** (1) is the primary factor in a leech's motion. Also pictured here is the mouth (B), the rear sucker (D) a cutaway portion of the body (C) and (E).

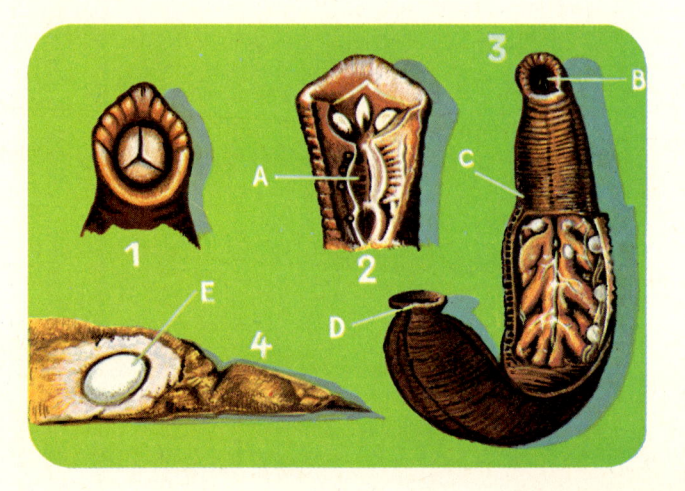

A **caterpillar** has a pair of legs on each of the first three segments behind its head and several pairs of pro-legs at the hind end of its body. As it moves, it holds on with the front legs, draws up the rear of its body and grips with the fleshy pro-legs, then pushes the front part of its body forward again.

is the water, and it can swim quite well; but its normal method of progression is by means of two suckers—one at each end of its body. Holding on with the hind sucker, the leech pushes the front of the body forward to full stretch and takes hold with the front sucker. The grip with the hind sucker is then relinquished and the body brought forward, the rear sucker then taking hold just behind the front sucker. So a leech loops along like a looper caterpillar, but using suckers instead of legs.

The starfish, along with some of its relatives such as the sea urchin and sea cucumber, has specialized in the use of suckers. Along the underside of each arm of a starfish is a groove, and in this lie hundreds of tube-feet, in rows. Each cylindrical tube-foot can be stretched out or contracted, and at its end is a sucker that can get a fair grip of the

214 / ANIMAL WORLD

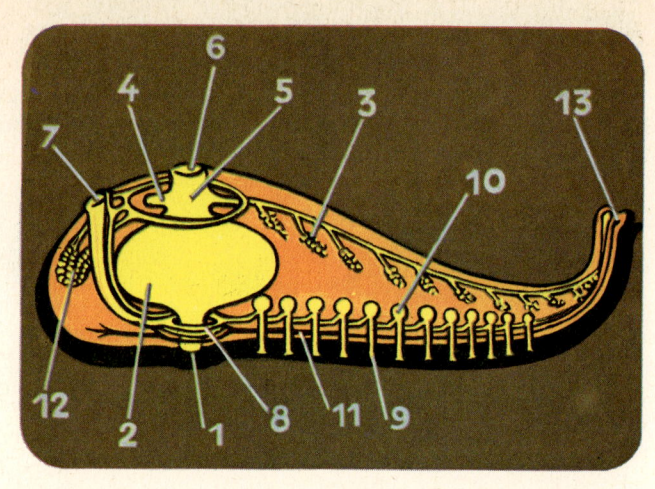

(above, left)
The **tube-feet** of the **starfish** are its means of locomotion. Each tube-foot acts independently of the others. It pushes out, takes hold and is then contracted. With hundreds of tube-feet in each arm doing this, the starfish is dragged along over the ocean floor.

(above, right)
In the **arm of a starfish** there is a groove that contains hundreds of **tube-feet,** aligned in rows. (9,10). Each foot can be extended and contracted. Other internal organs and nerves are also diagramed here (1-8, 11-13).

substratum. Often each acts independently of all the others—but they can also work more or less in unison to pull the starfish along.

It is interesting to note how varied can be the methods of progression used within a related group of animals. For example, a close relative of the starfish is the brittle-star. This has lost its tube-feet, but its five arms are longer and more slender than those of starfishes, and it wriggles its arms in a serpentine manner to make its way over rocks. So effective is this way of getting about that a brittle-star can even wriggle its way up a vertical face of rock.

Not only do animals have the organs necessary for responding to the impulse to move. They often have more than a single choice of the kind of motion they will adopt, and the medium in which to put their power of movement into effect. They may move over the ground, burrow into it, or they may climb. Animals living in water may also swim, and so do some land animals. In addition, some land animals fly, or glide through the air, as indeed do some aquatic animals, such as flying fishes. These are the most important, for to a large extent the organs of locomotion determine by their shape the animal's whole way of life; and in all main groups of animals we find species that are particularly adapted to one or another of these ways of getting about. They can also use the other parts of the body for muscular movement, such as for pushing out tentacles, moving jaws to feed, or moving the head to look around. But we have only the space to deal with movements involved in locomotion.

There are also species that move only to a very limited extent, as if the natural aspiration to movement has gone into reverse. We see an example of this in the relatives of starfishes known as sea lilies. These have five arms, or arms in multiples of five, as in starfishes; but they cease to move about once they are past the larval stage. Instead, a sea lily is stalked, and at the top of the stalk is the body proper, turned upside-down, with the arms reaching up to catch particles of food falling down through the water.

NATURE IN MOTION / 215

(left)
A **slug** travels over the ground on a fleshy part of the body known as its **foot.** This foot gives off slime continuously as the slug travels, so that the animal lays its own "road surface" as it goes. This facilitates its movements, especially over dusty ground.

However, a relative of the sea lilies, known as the feather star, has a stalk in the post-larval stage, but loses it. Instead of reverting to the habit of the starfish, and using its arms for locomotion, it retains the same relative position of the body as the sea lily, but walks about on short projecting parts known as cirri, with its feathered arms held upwards in the water, feeding in the same way as the sea lily.

When the impulse to move is present, an animal propels itself with whatever means it has. Without legs of some sort, only slow speeds are possible. The **wriggling motion** of snakelike reptiles, for example, is only a form of "crawling on the belly."

The Impulse to Move

PERHAPS THE MOST IMPORTANT CONCLUSION to be drawn from the animals so far considered is that, given the impulse to move, an organism will use whatever it has to assist movement. This may be a creeping movement with the whole body, as in an amoeba or a sponge, or with the "foot" as in snails and slugs, or with the base of the body as in a sea anemone. It may be crawling using bristles, as in an earthworm, or suckers as in a leech, tube-feet as in a starfish or cirri as in a feather star. Should any of these means become lost, as in a brittle-star, then the animal will wriggle. And we see the same in legless lizards and in snakes.

Only slow speeds are possible until something in the form of legs are developed. These are the organs that gave emancipation from "crawling on the belly". And a very real emancipation it is. Speed in running, the ability to jump to considerable heights and across broad gaps and, finally, flight all depend on some specialized development of these valuable outgrowths. And legs can also be used in swimming and for digging or burrowing.

In all the major groups of higher animals we find that in some form or other development has been along these five lines: walking, running and jumping, climbing, swimming, burrowing and flying.

Jointed legs make walking, running and jumping possible for the arthropods, which include insects, crustaceans, millepedes, centipedes, spiders and mites. This **house centipede** has 15 pairs of long legs that carry its body high off the ground when it runs.

(left)
A **spider** has four pairs of jointed legs, each consisting of seven segments. When it walks it moves the first and third legs on one side with the second and fourth on the other, and then it continues with the remaining legs.

(above)
On the **arm of a starfish** are tiny tube-feet with suckers at their ends, helpful for clinging to rocks in violent surf.

How Animals Walk

WALKING, TOGETHER WITH RUNNING AND JUMPING, which are no more than extensions of the walking action, is confined mainly to two groups of animals. The first group is the arthropods, or jointed-legged invertebrates. These include crabs, lobsters and prawns that live partly on the seabed, as well as land crustaceans such as land crabs and wood lice; insects; millipedes and centipedes; spiders and mites. The second group are vertebrates such as: the amphibians (frogs, toads and newts), lizards, birds and mammals.

When we walk we put one foot forward on the ground and use it as a fulcrum. We lever the body forward while advancing the other foot by swinging it, pendulum-like, from the hip. In running the legs are moved more quickly; the ball of the foot acts as the fulcrum and the stride is lengthened. Anyone who walks correctly, heel-and-toe with each foot in turn, will travel in a straight line, although in practice most people show a slight wobble of the body and this is reflected in the tracks they leave in sand or snow.

An insect appears to move in a perfectly straight line; but again appearances are deceptive. In fact, although it maintains a straight direction it zigzags to do so. It does not walk by moving each of its

218 / ANIMAL WORLD

(right)
An **insect** has three pairs of legs and walks by advancing the front and back legs of one side together with the middle leg of the other side. Then, while the weight rests on these three legs, the other three are swung forward, and so on. The movement is actually zigzagging rather than straight, and therefore it is not very efficient. Shown here is the common **blowfly** or **bluebottle.**

(center, right)
Impala are long-legged, medium-sized African antelope, agile and graceful. They live in herds of up to a hundred. When alarmed, the herd **leaps** in all directions, the leap of one single antelope measuring up to 35 feet.

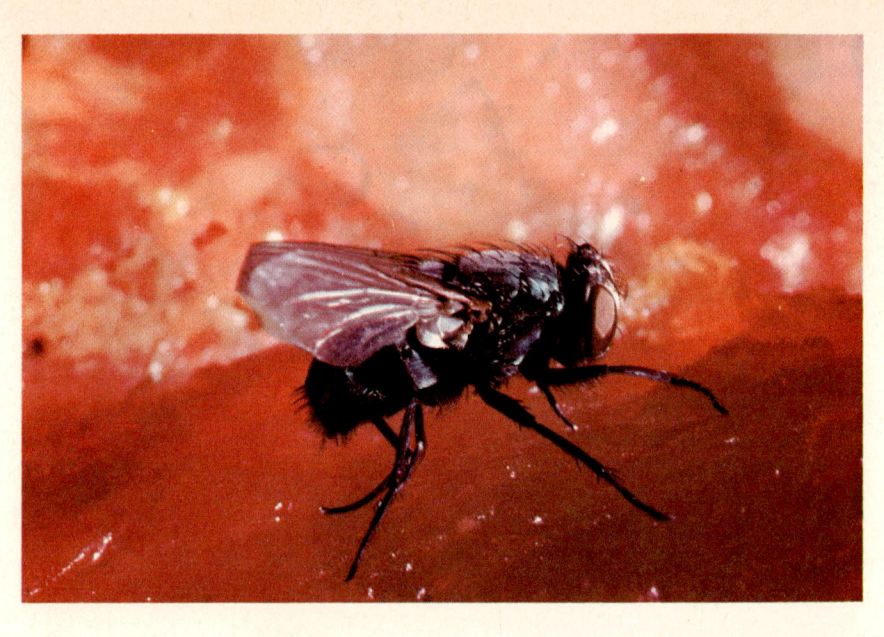

In changing from one form of movement to another, a **horse** (below) changes its leg patterns. Special **gaits,** such as pacing, are much-admired in horse shows. In this motion the two legs on each side move together. In the **canter,** the horse uses three legs together, with a foreleg leading. Shown here (bottom) bounding into the surf are the "sea-going" ponies of Ocracoke Island in North Carolina.

(left)
Most **crabs** move by walking across the sea bottom with their five pairs of **walking legs.** All that is needed for them to live on land is a change in their method of breathing. Some species live permanently on land but need to return to the water to breed.

three pairs of legs in turn but advances the fore and hind legs of one side and the middle leg of the other side almost simultaneously. As soon as the feet come to rest on the ground these three legs form a tripod which takes the weight of the body. The tripod also acts as the fulcrum lifting the body forward at the same time as the other three legs swing forward to form a second tripod. As each tripod is formed the insect's body is swung to left or right, as the case may be, producing a zigzagging movement. That this lateral movement results in a zigzag is an indication that energy is being used rather wastefully.

In the higher four-legged vertebrates there is greater efficiency although there is one pair of legs less. Not all move with the same efficiency, and not all use the same pattern of movement. This pattern is not always easy to set down in words. A horse walking, for example, puts the near hind foot forward, followed by the near fore foot, then the off hind and the off fore foot. The order of movement as well as the timing varies as the horse passes from a walk to a trot, a canter or a gallop. In the trot each diagonal pair of legs (near front and off hind, or vice versa) touches the ground together. The rhythm of the canter is near hind, near fore and off hind together, with the off fore leg leading. In the walk the body rises and falls, and this movement becomes accentuated as the horse passes into a trot, canter and finally into the bounding movement of a gallop.

Most four-legged animals use some similar pattern, although it varies in details from species to species, and it varies within a species according to speed (whether walking, trotting, cantering or galloping, although these terms are usually reserved for horses). There is, however, a movement known as pacing, in which the two legs on each side move together, as in a camel. This is more common than is usually supposed. A

(below)
Giraffes advance the legs of each side **alternately,** in contrast to the usual action of quadrupeds. Their long legs enable them to move fast, and when running they sometimes almost appear to float through the air.

(right)
The rough terrain of the Bad Lands and the Grand Canyon require great skill in motion. The high, **bounding gait** of the **mule deer** make it admirably suited to the broken and unpredictable land it inhabits. Although it is not as fast as the whitetail deer found in the eastern United States, its agility compensates for what it lacks in speed.

(below)
Many bipeds, including man, find **hopping** a slow, clumsy and tiring way to travel, but the **kangaroos** have become experts at it and can reach 30 m.p.h. or more.

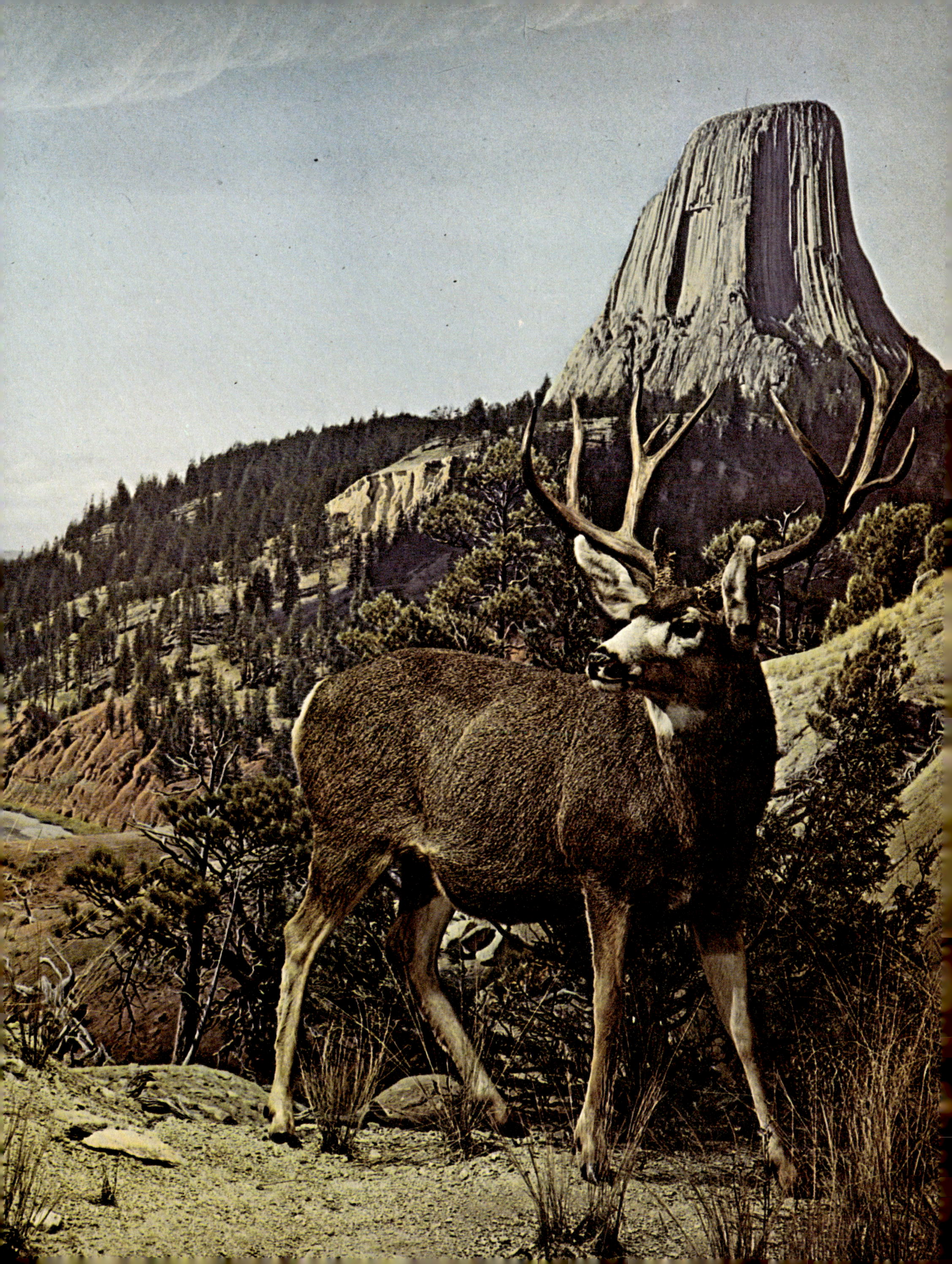

horse can be a pacer, and is then known as an ambler in England; pacing is much in vogue in the United States, in shows and trotting races. But a camel paces only when running, whereas a giraffe paces both when walking and running. The maned wolf of South America, foxlike and with stiltlike legs, paces when walking but not when running. Several kinds of antelope also use pacing at times.

Jumping—a Form of Running

JUMPING IS ALMOST ANOTHER FORM of running but with a powerful upthrust. The human jumper runs at his barrier and, pushing off with one foot, either rises into the air more or less vertically for a high jump or sails through the air for the long jump. Four-footed animals use the two hind legs for the upthrust. The hind legs of jumping animals, or of those that progress over the ground in long leaps, are very much lengthened and strengthened as compared with the front legs. This is typical of kangaroos and wallabies but is also a feature of hares.

(below)
As **tree kangaroos** jump along among the branches, their forelegs are barely visible, as they are so small that they are hidden in the fur when not being used. Only the powerful **hind legs** are necessary to propel these animals along.

(right)
Though **fleas** could hardly be classed as anything but pests, they are certainly among the most accomplished of the world's **jumpers**. Could you imagine a man jumping 299 times his own length?

NATURE IN MOTION / 223

(left)
Birds with **long legs,** such as these **sarus cranes,** are generally the best runners. Some better examples of fast, long-legged birds are the ostrich, emu, rhea and cassowary. All of the latter are extremely large and flightless, and all are extraordinarily swift runners. Indeed, they are often called the "running birds."

It reaches its highest expression in rodents such as the jerboas and the kangaroo rats, in which the hind legs are long and stiltlike and the front legs so small that they become hidden in the fur when the animal is jumping along.

As a rule, in an animal with all four legs more or less equal, the longer the legs the better it is as a runner. Similarly, long-legged birds are the best runners. This becomes strikingly evident in the case of flightless birds when one compares the tremendous running abilities of an ostrich with the awkward waddle of the short-legged penguin. However, some of the very swiftest land animals can maintain their best speed for only a few hundred yards, while others having only slightly less maximum speed have the quality of endurance. The cheetah is the best example of the first; the dog is a good example of the second. A cheetah gives up after a few hundred yards, while a dog will go for miles.

Similarly, while large kangaroos may not make spectacular jumps for their size, they can keep on jumping time after time. Large kangaroos, standing six feet high, usually do not clear fences more than five feet high, although occasionally one will be seen to clear nine feet. A grey squirrel, with body less than a foot long, will make a vertical jump of four feet or more from a standing position, and even a wood mouse,

(above)
The **jack rabbit** of North America is, strictly speaking, a hare. One difference between a hare and a real rabbit is that the hare has much longer **hind legs** and consequently can run faster and bound farther. When running slowly the hind legs have a characteristic stiltlike appearance.

224 / ANIMAL WORLD

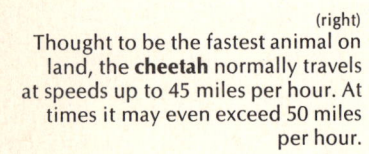

(right)
Thought to be the fastest animal on land, the **cheetah** normally travels at speeds up to 45 miles per hour. At times it may even exceed 50 miles per hour.

(below)
Frogs use their **leaping** ability for two purposes: to catch food and to escape from becoming food for their enemies. In a single leap their powerful hind legs can actually propel them many times their own length.

only a few inches long, will jump four feet upwards from a stationary position. This has some relation to the remark one often hears that if a man could jump as well as a flea he could jump over St. Paul's Cathedral. The larger the cross-section of the muscles the smaller is the output relative to the size of the animal. One result of this is that the smaller the animal the more quickly it will move. We have only to compare the extremely rapid movements of a shrew with those of an elephant to find an illustration of this. It also means that a man would pull his muscles apart in jumping proportionately as high as a flea.

All the same, the jumping abilities of medium-sized to large animals are quite spectacular. The bound, or long jump as it is called in athletics, may be as much as thirty-two feet in the great grey kangaroo. The white-tailed deer of North America can cover the ground in leaps of thirty or forty feet. A hare can clear twenty feet.

Records of Speeds

THERE IS A WIDE INTEREST in the speeds at which animals move and many tables have been published to show the relative speeds of animals on land, in the air and in water. However, the speed at which an animal moves is determined largely by incentive. With its life in immediate danger, an animal may well produce a burst of speed that is hard to estimate and quite impossible to time.

The cheetah is claimed to be the fastest animal on land. Not many years ago it used to be said that the top speed of a cheetah was 60 m.p.h. Recently, however, Dr. R. Bigalke, writing in *African Wild Life*, drew attention to three occasions when a cheetah has been timed against the speedometer of a car. The speeds registered were 45 m.p.h., 29 m.p.h. and 30 m.p.h. In the 1920s Mr. Gandar Dower organized a race between a cheetah and a greyhound on the racing track at Harringay, in London. The cheetah's maximum speed was 45 m.p.h. Dr.

Like a race horse called a "sprinter," the **cheetah** can only maintain its great speed for 15 or 20 seconds. But during these seconds it may cover a distance of a quarter mile.

The most abundant deer in North America, the **white-tailed deer** depends on its **swiftness** for safety. In addition to being a fast runner, it can jump 30 feet horizontally and eight feet high.

Grzimek has recorded 50 m.p.h. for a cheetah in Kenya. And Colonel Richard Meinertzhagen, in his *Kenya Diary,* published in 1957, gave 44 m.p.h. for the cheetah and 51 m.p.h. "when pressed by car on road over 200 yards". Now it is accepted, by all informed zoologists, that a cheetah normally travels at speeds up to 45 m.p.h. but may achieve 50 m.p.h. or slightly more if fully extended.

How Creatures Climb

CLIMBING IS EFFECTED mainly by four methods, and all four represent little more than a modified form of progression over the ground. The first of these is the simple act of crawling. A snail or slug ascends a wall or the trunk of a tree on its foot, as it would move over level ground; the trail of slime assists the mollusc in clinging to the vertical surface. The second method is the use of some form of claws to engage the irregularities of the surface in order to hold on. A millipede or centipede uses the clawlike endings to the legs but the claws are paired, one pair to each leg. Squirrels and other mammals also use their claws, as do climbing birds such as woodpeckers.

The third method uses some form of sucker on the foot or toes. In many insects there are, between the claws, one or more pads clothed with fine hollow bristles with expanded tips which are moistened by a secretion. On a rough surface the insect can climb using merely the claws. Should the surface be smooth to the point of being slippery the pads with their hollow hairs are pressed to the surface. There is some doubt about what happens then, but some entomologists incline to the view that the film of fluid between the hairs forms a minute pool on the surface, so that there is a temporary adhesion. This is broken as the insect alters the angle of the foot allowing air to flow between the surface and pads, thus setting the foot free to be lifted and moved forward again.

(below)
The treetops of the Amazon jungle are the home of the **sakiwinki monkey.** Remarkably agile, it takes great leaps from one tree to another, and it can run along a horizontal branch on its hind legs with its arms held high above its head. It can also hang upside down by its feet.

(below, left)
Toes are sometimes an important element in motion. Leaping from tree to tree is greatly aided by clinging toes, such as a **tarsier** has, that grasp the branches as the animal jumps.

(below, right)
Swinging through the trees, the **spider monkey** has an added limb to assist it—its long **tail.** When reaching high for another branch, the tail sometimes acts as an extra hand.

Suckers, which enable a starfish to cling to a rock, also enable it to climb up a vertical rock face, or even the glass side of an aquarium. An octopus will use the suckers on its arms to the same ends. Suckers in a variety of forms are found elsewhere in the animal kingdom. The fish known as the remora, sometimes called a ship-holder or shark-sucker, has a large sucker on its head which is a modified dorsal fin. With this it can hitchhike by fastening itself to the body of a large fish, or to any other moving object such as a ship. The sucker is oval, with a number of transverse plates having the hinder edges free, the whole being surrounded by a membranous border. When the remora places the sucker against a solid surface a slight erection of the hinder edges of the plates creates a series of suction chambers. The sucker can be freed only by the remora's moving forward or sideways. The result is that the remora becomes more firmly held as the fish or ship carrying it rushes through the water, but can free itself voluntarily by swimming forward.

Another aid to adhesion is seen in the feet of a gecko, a form of lizard. The underside of each of its flattened toes is furnished with transverse plates, but it seems that no suction is used nor any adhesive secretion; the plates are furnished with rows of minute hooks that catch in the very smallest irregularities of the surface. With a completely smooth surface a gecko cannot maintain its hold. Those species of geckos that have clinging pads can climb vertical walls or walk upside-down across a ceiling, as a fly does.

In some climbing animals sucker-like or clinging toes are combined with the habit of taking long leaps from tree to tree, as in the tarsier of the Philippines, Borneo and Sumatra, or with webbed toes as in the flying frog of Malaya, the toes with their webs spread wide during a leap giving enough parachute-like buoyancy to the light body of the frog to extend the range of the leap.

The fourth method of climbing is very like that used by a man to climb a rope, except that the limbs are only partially wrapped around the tree. It is the kind of climbing we expect to see in koalas and bears. On the other hand, the South Sea islanders climb coconut trees by holding the trunk with the hands and using the feet as in walking while the hands grip and are moved up hand-over-hand. Monkeys, too, use this method at times, although usually they leap up to take a hand-hold.

Although four categories of climbing have been enumerated it would be impossible to treat them as absolutely distinct. Were it possible to examine every climbing species, other less commonly used methods would be discovered, and it would be found that there is often overlapping, in which two or more of these patterns of climbing are used by a single animal. In addition we would need to consider how great an advantage it is for an animal to have grasping hands and feet, and also how often the prehensile tail, used as a fifth hand, comes into play to assist the limbs.

Movement in Water

IT HAS OFTEN BEEN SAID that swimming is virtually a matter of walking or running in water. If we say that for any given species progress through water is effected by methods not unlike those used for progress on land, then the statement is more nearly correct. But the more realistic method of approach is from the other direction; by tracing the evolution of locomotion through water we can see how locomotion on land sprang from it.

A proportion of the invertebrate animals living in the sea are able, as we have seen, to swim by what are, in effect, creeping movements, usually sinuous or snakelike. Certain sea slugs and sea snails live permanently in the surface waters of the open oceans. They have much the same equipment as their relatives that creep over the seabed or crawl on land. The wave-movements in the foot are hardly more pronounced, but they suffice to carry the animal along besides keeping it afloat. Many marine worms swim by the same sinuous movements as those which they use to creep over the seabed.

From this point there is a divergence in pattern. In one direction there are the shrimps, prawns and lobsters that have a rigid body combined with swimming legs and use a powerful flick of the tail when a vigorous propulsive movement is needed. Turtles with the body similarly enclosed in a rigid box propel themselves with flippers. Along the other path there is the fishlike swimming in which the body works much in the same way as does that of a snake on land. Used by the majority of fishes, this is most evident in eels and is also seen in otters and some seals.

While the sinuous or wriggling movements of the body, aided by the vertical tail fin, are the principal means by which fishes swim, in some species the fins assist, and in others the fins alone are the means of locomotion. In skates and rays the enlarged pectoral fins are used al-

Climbing up a tree is no more difficult for a **snail** than walking along the ground. A trail of slime helps it to achieve the necessary adhesion.

most as wings. In trunkfishes and cofferfishes, with the body a rigid box, only the fins and the tail are used for propulsion. The same is true of sea horses; for them the dorsal fin, worked almost like a propeller, is the only means of locomotion.

Many groups of typically marine animals have representatives that have come on land to live. Those such as the worms, which crawl on the seabed or swim with a crawling movement, have representatives that crawl on land. Those such as the crabs, which walk on the seabed or use their legs for swimming, have relatives that walk on land. In all these instances the transition from an aquatic swimming life to a terrestrial walking way of life has been moderately easy.

A typical fish has a tail fin, a pair of pectoral or breast fins, a pair of pelvic fins and median unpaired fins. Except for the tail fin, these are mainly used as balancers. Some fishes, such as the batfishes and frogfishes, have pectoral fins shaped almost like arms and quite literally hop with them over the seabed. The mudskippers are fishes that readily leave the water and hop over the mud when the tide is out. They use their pectoral fins as limbs and the tail for giving a push forward.

Watching a batfish or a frogfish hopping over the seabed it is easy to imagine how little more is needed to produce the four-legged animal capable of moving over land. The greater changes needed are those concerned with the breathing, from gill breathing to lung breathing.

We can therefore, and with greater truth, reverse the usual statement and say that walking is a modified swimming action. However, the whole of this process must be seen as reversible; almost any land animal entering water voluntarily or falling into water accidentally will instinctively use its normal means of locomotion on land to survive, and as a consequence will swim. Exceptions are man, frogs and monkeys. The last two use a breaststroke which is unlike any means of progression they use on land. Man has to make an even greater adjustment to his actions to swim.

Animals now living wholly or almost wholly in water, whose ancestors were land-living, tend to revert to the typical fishlike wriggling of the body in swimming. An otter, for example, runs on land like any other quadruped but folds its legs against its body and swims with sinuous motions through the water. Whales, by contrast, use an up-and-

opposite page:
(top row, left)
A **spider crab** crawls across the sea bottom on its long legs. It disguises itself by attaching seaweed to its hairy shell.

(top row, right)
A rapid-moving propellerlike **fin** is the only means of locomotion for the **seahorse.** Its tail is used to cling to undersea vegetation when hiding from its enemies.

(bottom left)
Turtles use their **"flippers"** to propel themselves through the water. Their inability to move rapidly has made them easy prey for man, and some species are now close to extinction.

(bottom right)
Diving ducks must **run** along the surface of the water to become airborne. This characteristic is a great help in identifying this group of birds.

(left)
Fresh water "dabbling" **ducks** have the ability to **spring** into the air and fly off immediately. This means a faster escape is possible and allows them to use small ponds and pot-holes.

down movement of the tail, which has horizontal flukes. This leads us to one of the more interesting discoveries of recent years, which is worth considering at length.

The Porpoise—a Puzzle

For years whales, dolphins and porpoises have puzzled scientists. Theoretically even the fastest of these, the dolphins and porpoises, should be unable to swim faster than ten knots, but there are many reliable observations which show that a porpoise can travel at twenty knots or more, and keep it up for about a half-hour.

The theoretical speed is calculated from muscular power, length, weight, surface area and drag coefficient (that is, the braking effect water has on a body moving through it). But as the observed facts of a porpoise's speed seem to contradict theory, some of the theoretical assumptions would seem to be wrong.

Theoretically, to be able to swim at twenty knots, a porpoise would need to produce seven per cent of one horsepower per pound of muscle. When we consider that dogs, horses and humans produce only one per cent of one horsepower per pound of muscle, such a figure is unacceptable. Physically, it is also improbable. The greater the power produced by a set of muscles, the higher the body temperature rises. With it an increased supply of oxygen to the muscles is needed, necessitating good respiratory and circulatory systems. Although these systems in the porpoise are efficient, they are not so efficient as all that. In addition the animal's covering of blubber retains heat, and so creates a ventilation problem that puts the animal at a disadvantage.

The accuracy of the theoretical demands depended above all on the

(bottom left)
Trout and salmon are able to make enormous **leaps** out of the water because of the powerful muscles in their tails. In doing so, the tail is brought to one side and then straightened out with a snap to drive the fish upwards.

(bottom center)
The yellow-headed **jawfish** can remain almost vertical in the water using its breast **fins as stabilizers.** When burrowing, it hovers vertically over the mouth of the burrow, diving tail-first into it at the first sign of danger.

(bottom right)
Although the **otter** is a quadruped that can run well on land, it is at its best in water. When swimming fast the legs are pressed into the sides of the body, and body and tail move with a **serpentine action.**

(left)
Generally a water creature, the **duckbill** or **platypus** swims by means of its **webbed feet.** The webs extend beyond the toes, but when the platypus goes on land it can fold the front part of the web back to give itself greater freedom in the use of the feet.

(above)
Like all lobsters, the **langousta** has five pairs of **walking legs** on the front half of the body and several pairs of much smaller **swimming legs** on the underside of the tail. Actual propulsion through the water, however, is by powerful flicks of the tail

correctness of the value for drag coefficient; this had been obtained from towing rigid models through water. It was just possible, however, that water had a less braking effect on living porpoises than on rigid models. To test this, foam rubber models were made, containing rods that could be mechanically flexed, to simulate a porpoise's swimming movements. The models were towed through water on which floated opaque particles, the movements of which could be photographed. The photographs showed that the drag was much less than with the rigid models, since the particles moved past them in parallel lines, whereas there had been eddies and turbulence around the rigid models, and it is these that cause drag, so reducing speed. It would seem therefore that a porpoise's undulations help to lessen the turbulences.

However, it had also been observed that on the skin of porpoises accelerating or stopping suddenly, there appeared transitory ripple-like folds of the skin, vertical and stationary, chiefly on the sides and underparts of the animal. It was suggested that these, too, helped to accommodate unequal water pressure and reduce drag.

It had also been discovered that the porpoise's skin is particularly well supplied with capillaries in areas subjected to the greatest turbulence. It has been suggested that at these points there is a much increased loss of body heat to the water, so cooling the porpoise, and that in some way they helped to reduce friction.

The degree of drag is determined at the "boundary layer"; that is, the band of water particles and the skin cells that separate the porpoise from the surrounding water. Reduction of friction here would make higher speeds possible.

In 1955 Dr. M. Kramer discovered that a porpoise's skin consists of two layers, a hard fatty layer overlaid by a soft layer, comprising numerous vertical ducts, filled with spongy, water-logged tissue. He suggested that this layer absorbs friction, so allowing the water to flow more smoothly over the body, making possible an increase in speed.

To test this, he made a model of the porpoise's skin, using rubber sheets separated by tiny rubber studs, and filled the spaces between with fluids of varying viscosities. The skin was put on model porpoises and when tested showed a reduction of drag by as much as sixty per cent.

This is probably not the complete answer. There may be subsidiary factors to be considered, but so far as can be seen at present the practical result is that a porpoise is able to travel at what seems an incredibly high speed, simply because it has a highly efficient, built-in, anti-friction mechanism.

If anything, there is a greater general interest in the speeds of fishes than in the speeds of land animals. It is a surprising fact that porpoises and dolphins are faster than was at one time thought theoretically possible. It is of interest to recall that ships' captains and other observers on fast ships have long claimed that dolphins and porpoises could travel at 30 m.p.h. They were judging this by comparison with the speeds of their own ships. What we now need to see is whether the discovered speeds of fishes stand up to scientific scrutiny.

Speeds of Fishes

SPEEDS WELL IN EXCESS of 30 m.p.h. have been claimed for such fishes as swordfish, marlin and sailfish, which have been credited with 68, 70 and 71 m.p.h. respectively. Many years ago two Canadians, Earl Thompson and Bob Edge, designed what they called a fish-o-meter, which included the speedometer from a motorcycle. When they hooked

(below, left)
Not a rapid swimmer, the **Arctic beluga** undulates through the water, sometimes single file, occasionally two or three abreast. It is rarely seen at the surface, showing little of itself even when it comes up to blow at regular intervals.

(below, right)
The **walrus** is a kind of seal that lives in the Arctic on the ice floes. A cumbrous swimmer, it is, however, a good diver. It feeds on mollusks and crustaceans on the ocean floor. When hauling itself onto the ice its flippers are used to press its body up and out of the water.

The **fur seals** of the North Pacific, also known as sea bears, spend most of their time at sea. They breed on islands off the coast of Alaska and then spread out, some traveling hundreds of miles.

a tuna and allowed it to run, its speed was registered at 44 m.p.h. Tuna belong to the same suborder, *Scombroidea,* as the swordfish, marlin and sailfish, which means they are all the same type of fishes. More recently Harry L. Fierstine measured the speed of yellowfin tuna and wahoo, both scombroids, and obtained with a more refined apparatus speeds that varied from some 12 m.p.h. to 50 m.p.h. These still leave us in doubt about the speeds of marlin, sailfish and swordfish, but as they have more elegant lines than the tuna and wahoo it is probable that they top these speeds; yet it is doubtful whether they do so by as much as 10 to 20 m.p.h.

Although one may say, for purposes of brief description, that a fish swims by wriggling its body, that must necessarily be an oversimplification. The important part of their propulsion through water lies in the powerful thrusting movement given by the caudal peduncle, that is the hinder part of the body which carries the tail fin. It is a powerful thrust with the caudal peduncle, also, that enables a fish to dart suddenly from danger, and that carries a fish into the air clear of water, as when a salmon leaps for a fly or ascends a weir. Whales and dolphins also leap out of water using this jackknife type of thrust. A flying fish,

Like all penguins, the **adelie** is adapted for swimming, the front limbs being modified to flippers. Penguins walk with a kind of shuffling gait; to travel quickly they flop onto their bellies, push with their feet and toboggan along.

(right)
Bats are the only mammals that truly **fly.** Their front limbs have extremely long digits, across which is spread a thin membrane of skin, and these form the **wings.** In addition, a special method of detecting their prey, echo-location, enables them to catch insects at night or at twilight. Other mammals that are said to fly, such as flying squirrels, do not have wings like birds and bats and can only glide through the air.

(far right)
Dragonflies are powerful and agile flyers because each wing of the two pairs they possess works independently. In many four-winged insects the wings are coupled in flight by a kind of hook and eye, but in dragonflies **each wing is free of the others.**

by contrast, gathers speed by swimming at speed obliquely upwards. Then, as its body clears the water, it taxis over the surface with a rapid sculling action of the lower lobe of its tail fin, and at last becomes airborne.

Maximum figures suggested for the performances of flying fishes are that the flight may be sustained for 40 seconds, the fish soaring to a height of 30 feet and travelling a distance of up to a quarter of a mile. Usually the flights are much shorter and the height reached between three and six feet. The speed in air of a flying fish averages 35 m.p.h., being about 40 m.p.h. at the start and slowing to 25 m.p.h. at the finish.

Spectacular as these figures are, the flight of a flying fish must take its place with the performance of flying frogs, flying squirrels and others, that merely glide. It is not true flight as seen in insects, birds and bats, which remain airborne powered by the beating of the wings. These three types of animals alone are capable of true flight, and the formation of the wings differs in all three.

The wings of insects are outgrowths of the cuticle on the dorsal surface of the segments forming the thorax. These segments are three in number, and in fossil dragonflies from the Carboniferous period there are three pairs of wings, the first pair being only small. In some modern insects, such as flies, there is only one pair of wings, the last pair being reduced to small knobs, known as halteres or balancers.

In birds the wing is formed from the bones of the forelimb, with the loss of most of the finger bones, the limb being beset with long flight feathers. In bats the fingers are much elongated and a web of skin extending across the fingers to the flanks constitutes the wing membrane.

In all these three groups of animal fliers there is a range of variations in shape and in methods of functioning similar to the range in airplanes. This is not surprising since all must work on the same aerodynamic principles. Thus in flying animals we find large wings, usually linked with slow beats, where lift is required, as when the insect, bird or bat has a large body; broad wings for soaring flight; short wings for maneuverability; and long narrow wings for speed.

NATURE IN MOTION / 235

(above)
Hummingbirds developed several thousand years before helicopters were invented and can do things that their mechanical counterparts still cannot do. Their wings may beat as fast as 200 times per second.

(top left)
A number of animals are capable of **leaping,** but often the action is too rapid to see without the aid of a high-speed camera. In this picture a small **Australian mouse** has been caught mid-leap.

(center left)
Flying squirrels do not really fly, as does the bat. Instead they merely **glide** from branch to branch.

(bottom left)
While **flying fish** often give spectacular performances, they do not really fly, but rather shoot into the air and glide.

In taking off, a bird uses the full stroke of the wings, raising them over its back until their tips almost touch, then bringing them forward, down and back. At the same time it crouches and pushes off with the legs. The tail may give lift in the takeoff but its main role is as a rudder. As a bird comes in to land it tilts the body up, throws the legs forward, fans its tail to act as a brake and, at the moment just before touch-down, swings the wings forward.

The most highly skilled fliers are hummingbirds and, among insects, the hoverflies. Both can hover, fly forwards or backwards or sideways, as well as up and down. In both, the wings in flight are a blur, they move so quickly. In some species of hummingbirds the wing movement may reach as much as 200 beats a second.

Speeds of up to 200 m.p.h. have been measured for the cloud swift. A peregrine falcon may reach 180 m.p.h., but only when swooping at its prey. Estimates for level flight give the fastest birds as the lammergeier, diver or loon and racing pigeon, with speeds of 79.5, 90 and 94.3 m.p.h. respectively. Apart from these the more carefully contrived records of speed give only water fowl and certain birds of prey, in addition to the three already mentioned, as achieving 60 m.p.h. or more. Most birds do not exceed 40 m.p.h.

The last form of locomotion is burrowing by digging tunnels in the

(left)
Coming in for a **landing,** the **sea eagle** tilts upward and throws its legs forward. It uses its tail as a brake and, at the last moment, swings its wings forward.

(right)
Equipped with oversized and well-developed **jumping legs,** a **grasshopper** can jump away from most approaching dangers. Some species have wings as well and are good flyers.

(right)
Petrels feed by picking up squid, fish and dead animals from the surface of the sea. In flying they keep their webbed feet close to the surface of the waves, their legs dangling as if they were walking on water.

(left)
Graceful in flight, the **osprey** or **fish hawk** soars and wheels over the water on its slightly crooked wings, watching for fish. In catching its prey it rockets down to the water, extends its legs forward and impales the fish on its long talons. The action is similar to the one shown here, where it is landing in its nest.

(right)
A North American **chickadee,** one of the tit family, is pictured here, coming in to land at a bird table. The ends of the wings are splayed to give a braking effect, and the legs are thrown forward to act as a landing carriage.

earth, using the claws. This reaches its highest expression in moles. A mole's body is almost cylindrical, with all appendages, such as ears, that might protrude and so impede progress, reduced in size or lost altogether. The limbs are shortened and the bones enormously strengthened, and the front limbs bear broad hands furnished with stout claws, making an efficient combination of pick and shovel.

Finally, it is worth mentioning the intention movement. This may be such a slight movement as almost to escape observation—almost, but not quite. It is the movement associated with preparations of the body by the muscles for making certain movements, which then stop short of the

(right)
Largest of the North American **swans,** the trumpeter's wingspan may reach 10 feet and its weight 35 pounds. In order to take off, these birds must run over the water for a considerable distance.

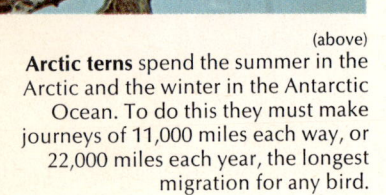

(above)
Arctic terns spend the summer in the Arctic and the winter in the Antarctic Ocean. To do this they must make journeys of 11,000 miles each way, or 22,000 miles each year, the longest migration for any bird.

(right)
Gulls can soar well, riding the conventional currents that rise over cliffs, buildings or the sea, or those from the stern of a ship. Bird wings are formed from the forelimb bones, with flight feathers added. Strong wings are needed for this **ring-billed gull,** for it breeds on the Great Lakes and goes southward to salt water for the winter.

intended movement. For example, when a bird is about to take off it first starts to crouch, preparing for the push-off, and there is a slight lifting of the wings. A bird will do these two things at the slightest alarm, but if the alarm does not develop its body goes back to the normal position. Even these slight movements, however, show there was the intention to fly, had the need arisen. When one bird does this others around see it and themselves prepare for flight, which is why we so often see all the birds take off simultaneously as if on a word of command.

Animals and humans are using intention movements all day long. Among those animals with eyes intention movements constitute a form of language, a means of communication of intention, as when birds all fly off together. And among the many features and characteristics that distinguish animal from plant, intention movements form one of the most decisive.

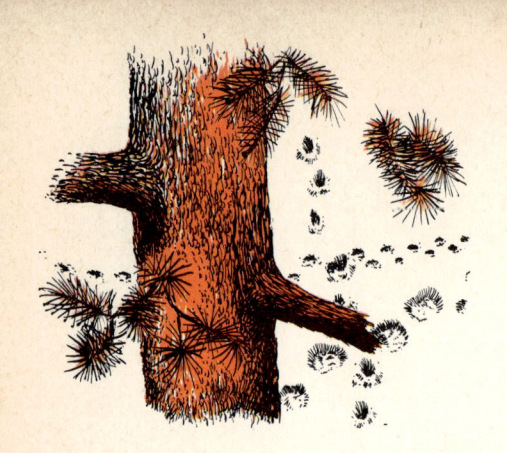

▶ *What you can tell about animals from the clues and footprints they leave behind.*

Tracks and Trails

MAN CONSIDERS HIMSELF to be superior to all other creatures because he has gained ascendancy over them. Man's brain, which enables him to think of new ideas, and his opposable thumb, which gives him the ability to hold the tools needed to carry out these ideas, have allowed him to gain this ascendancy. They have also enabled him to build the civilization which has changed his way of living so completely. While modern man no longer has to hunt wild creatures for food, it is also true that no longer is he able to compete with the wild creatures on an equal footing. Civilization, which has given modern man many things, has also robbed him of some and dulled his basic five senses.

We notice this every time we go out into the woods and fields and complain about the lack of wildlife. It is true that civilization has reduced the number of wild creatures, but there are still far more of them than we ever see. And for every creature that we see on our trips afield, at least a hundred of them see us. Our senses of sight, hearing and smell have been dulled by lack of use and by abuse to a point where we are really handicapped. The wild creatures must constantly use their senses to survive; they use them to avoid man. Man is a predator, and his habits and the spread of his civilization have caused many diurnal creatures to become nocturnal in order to hide themselves under the protective cover of darkness. It is small wonder that so many of us see so little.

Yet we can see more. We can train ourselves to see more and we can learn to interpret correctly what we do see. Although we cannot change the animals' habits so that we can see the creatures themselves,

Tracking an animal involves more than just having a good pair of field glasses to spot it. Although the animal itself may remain unseen, it leaves various signs throughout its habitat which show that it is around or that it has been nearby recently. Footprints, claw marks on trees, tufts of fur, and the print of a dragged tail are all among the clues that the alert woodsman uses to determine which animals inhabit the land about him.

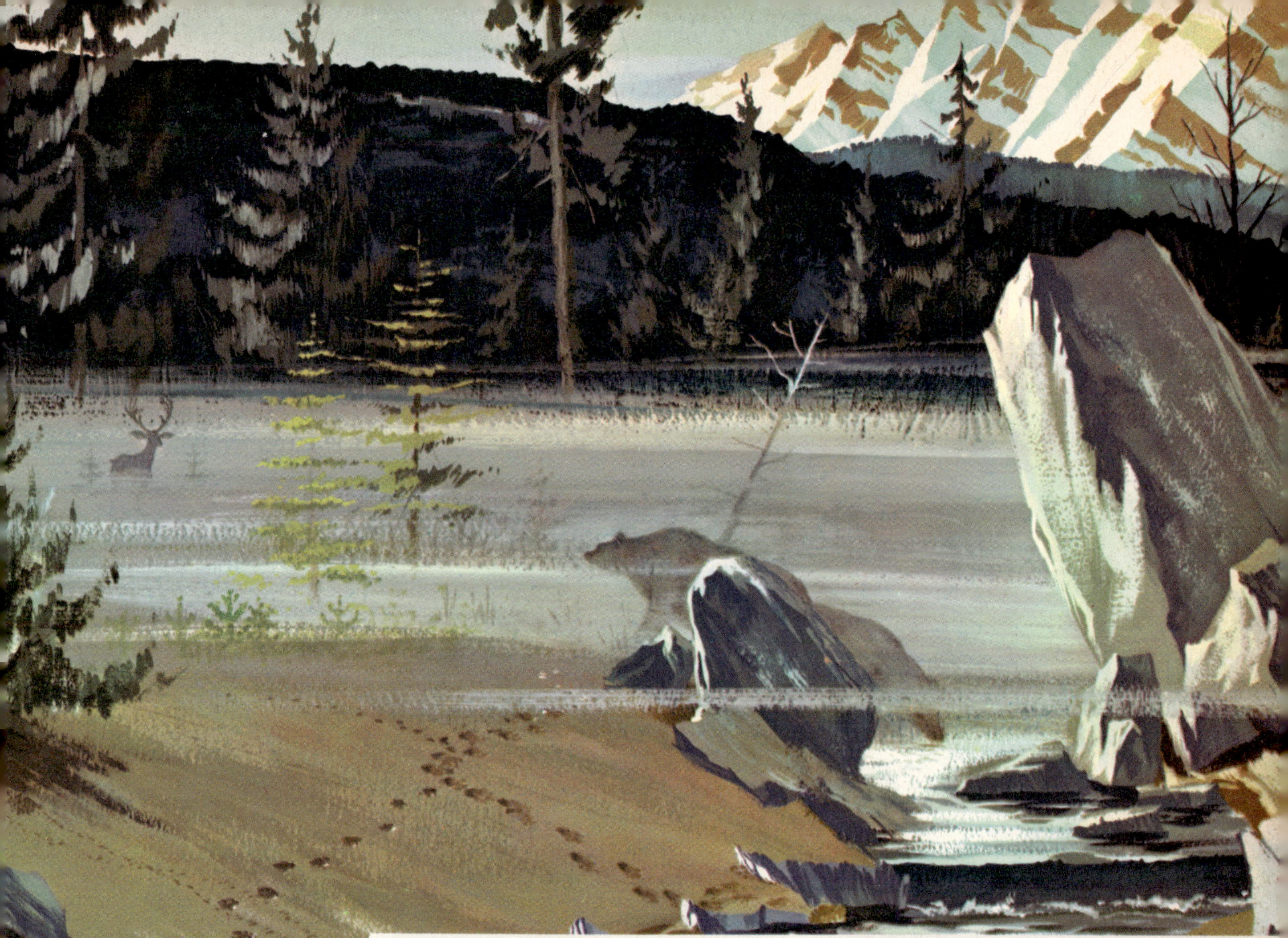
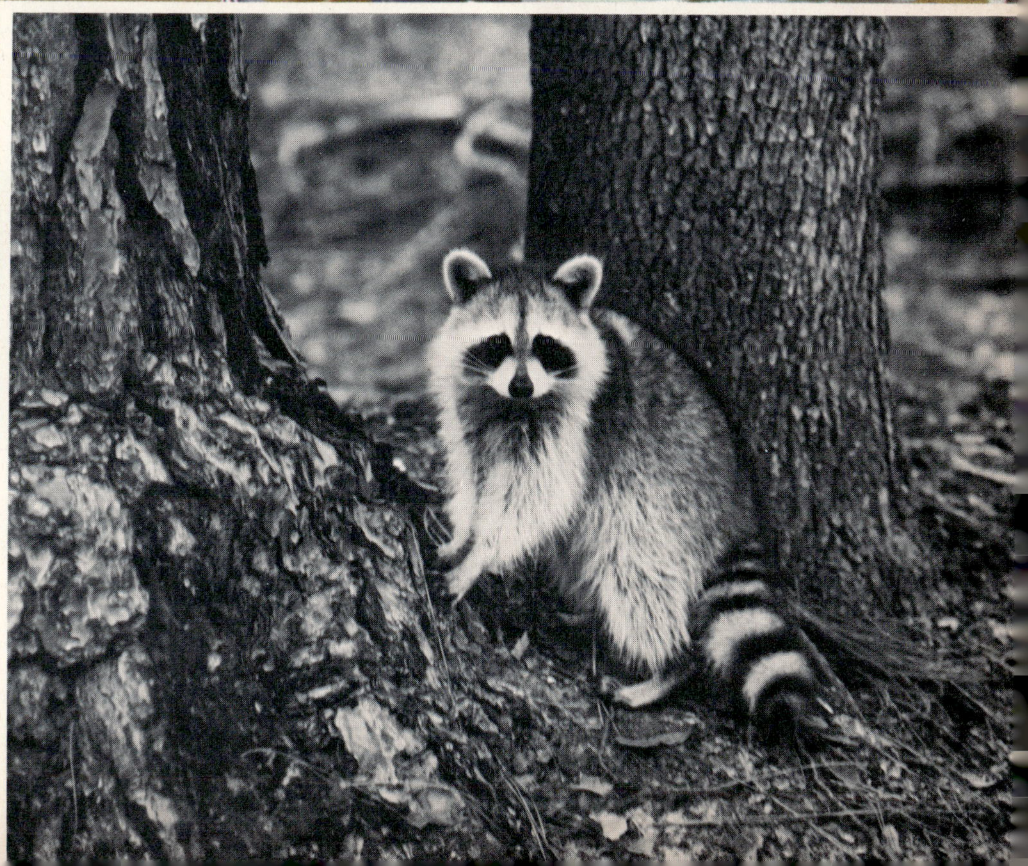

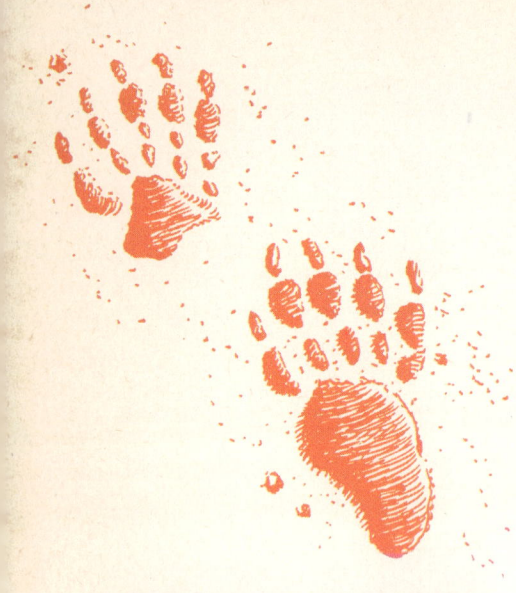

we can learn to read the tracks and sign which they all leave behind. The tracking ability of primitive people is well known. The Indians of North America, the bushmen of Africa and the aborigines of Australia are the world's most famous trackers. The tracking ability of the aborigines borders on the phenomenal. Although we can never hope to compete with these primitive people we can learn enough about tracks and trails to have a whole new world open up for us.

The Process of Elimination

THE ACTUAL FOOTPRINTS of an animal are the most common marks that we will encounter but we must not believe that they are the only things to look for. Much of what an animal does is recorded. Its home, its range, its food, its tracks, its droppings are all signs which we must look for.

First we must learn all we can about all the creatures which inhabit the region in which we intend to do our tracking. We must know what type of animal each one is, what size it is, what kind of food it eats and where it should be found. One of the big secrets of tracking is the process of elimination. In other words the animals which will not fit into the particular situation must be eliminated from consideration.

For example, let us assume that we are following a set of four tracks in the snow which wind along a fence row. The hind feet tracks register in front of the front feet but the front feet are almost paired

(above and top)
The **raccoon** is found in wooded country near streams. It is nocturnal, playful, agile and omnivorous. Before eating, it often dabbles its food in water.

(right)
Since the **grey squirrel** was imported to England, its **tracks** there are as familiar as in the United States. Unafraid of man, this rodent can be seen in city parks and suburban areas.

together. A rabbit's tracks may look like this because his front feet fall one behind the other only when he is moving rapidly. When the tracks stop at a tree, we can eliminate the rabbit and settle for a squirrel, because the squirrel can climb and the rabbit cannot. Now what kind of squirrel was it? Throughout the state of New Jersey, for example, there are only three kinds of squirrels, the red, the gray and the flying squirrel. Naturally, then, we would not think of a fox squirrel; it is not found here. It would not be the flying squirrel, because it seldom travels on the ground and when it does it leaves side marks made by the drag of its flight webs. The gray squirrel is larger than the red squirrel but a large red squirrel will make as big a track as a small gray squirrel.

What do we do now? Like Sherlock Holmes, we must look around for further evidence. Perhaps we are able to find a walnut which the squirrel has removed from its cache and opened. If so, we are in luck. A red squirrel, having smaller teeth than does the gray, usually makes four separate cuts, one in each quarter of the nut, while the gray squirrel makes only two cuts. It is by this elimination and deduction that we can learn the animal's identity.

Tracks in Snow and Mud

OF ALL THE MEDIUMS suitable for tracking, snow is best; since it covers everything, the animal can be followed no matter where it goes. Some snow conditions are much better than others. A wet snow

Tracks in wet snow are the easiest to follow. Here, in Yellowstone Canyon, the deep wet snow of March provides **ideal tracking conditions.**

Dingos have been the aboriginals' companions for nearly 6,000 years. These dogs are credited with wiping out the Tasmanian devil and the pouched wolf on the Australian mainland.

The **Siberian lynx** is a tireless walker, a poor runner and a good swimmer. Its **broad feet** afford an advantage in moving on snow.

of an inch depth is perfect. The tracks will be sharp and clean and sometimes of two shades, if the animal is heavy enough for its tracks to cut through the snow and let some of the brown earth show through. Deep wet snow is also good but it may freeze, forming a crust which will enable animals to walk over the top without a trace. Shallow dry snow is only fair, because the tracks are seldom distinct and the slightest wind will cause the snow to drift and distort the tracks. Deep dry snow is poor, for the animal in pulling its feet out of the snow will disturb the snow so that it settles back in over the track marks, obliterating them. In deep snow about all that is available is the pattern of the animal's foot placement. While this is enough for an experienced tracker, it causes trouble for the novice.

Mud makes the most perfect track, revealing all the detail in each footprint. Mud, however, is mainly restricted to the edges of seas, ponds, lakes and rivers. If the animal wanders away from this narrow wet belt we lose it. Occasionally after a rainstorm dirt roads and ploughed fields make good mud tracks, but again when the animal walks up through the grass we lose it.

Dust will also yield very good tracks, but they are easily disturbed by the wind. Grains of sand are constantly shifting so that tracks in sand are soon softened or obliterated. Hard rock areas make tracking almost an impossibility, although the aborigines of Australia can follow tracks across rock which no one else can find.

There are several additional things to remember in dating tracks. Tracks in mud can be dated from the last rain which wiped the slate clean. Each additional sunny day dries out the mud, and the longer the time, the more cracks appear in the dried mud. An animal walking in soft mud will often give the impression of being larger than it really is because the feet have a tendency to flatten or splay in soft mud, creating a larger print. Snow tracks can be dated back to the last snowfall. Snow tracks grow larger on warm days because of the melting. The snow then freezes at night and forms an ice glazing inside the track. This can also help to age the track. Recollection of the last windy day will help to find the age of tracks made in soft snow and dust.

One thing which may confuse the amateur tracker is the fact that many animals in walking will place a hind foot on top of the track of the forefoot, either completely covering it or showing all of the hind foot and just a part of the front foot. The forefoot track of any of the predatory animals is seldom seen because, as an old saying goes, "A perfect stalker is a perfect walker". This means that an animal which stalks its prey must walk silently and be careful where it places its feet. The predators are careful in placing the front feet and then, to avoid having to do the job twice, place the hind feet in the identical spots that the front feet were in. A track of a red fox walking in snow looks like a dotted line on a piece of paper, so perfectly are the tracks aligned.

Knowledge of the physical characteristics of the animals is also important in observing tracks. Hoofed animals walk on their toenails and usually show only one or two nail prints. Plantigrade animals such as the bear, the raccoon and the skunk walk on the flat of their feet like man and show the entire foot and usually five toes on each foot. Most of the rodents, which are also plantigrade, show the five toes on the hind foot but usually only four toes on the front foot. Most of the carnivores of the dog and the cat families are toe walkers but show only four toes on both the front and the hind foot. In the case of the dog family, the toenails show in the tracks because they are non-retractable. The cat family has retractable claws and the nails do not show in the tracks; one exception is the cheetah, whose claws are only partially retractable. Some of the long-tailed animals such as the muskrat, beaver and porcupine drag their tails, while others such as the fox and the wolf carry them jauntily aloft.

The comparative size of the front foot to the hind foot also varies. It depends on the type of walker the animal is and where the bulk of the weight is placed in its body. For these reasons some animals have larger front feet than they do back feet and vice versa.

In following tracks, it is helpful to walk on the side opposite from the sun, so that the tracks are in a slight shadow.

Hoofed Animals

OF ALL THE ANIMAL tracks, those of the hoofed animals are the easiest to follow, for they register on everything except solid rock and ice. The hoofed animals are among the largest of our animals and the combination of their weight and their sharp hoofs causes excellent prints. The family *Bovidae* contains some of the heaviest of the land animals and includes most of our domestic animals such as cattle, sheep and goats. In fact a good place to start tracking would be in some

(bottom left)
Dragging its tail behind it, the **muskrat** leaves **tail prints** as well as footprints. The trails are usually well defined because muskrats live along muddy river banks.

(bottom right)
Wolves, the largest members of the dog family, carry their tails upright. Almost at the point of extinction in Europe, they can still be found in the United States. They hunt in packs, each member helping to bring a larger animal down.

246 / ANIMAL WORLD

The **bighorn** is the only wild sheep of North America. The ram carries horns that form a spiral and, like the ewe, is buff to brown with a white tail patch.

farmer's barnyard. The large hoofprints of the domestic cow are very similar to the tracks made by the bison of the United States and Canada, the wisent of Europe, the gaur of Burma, the yak of Mongolia, the musk ox of the arctic and the cape buffalo of Africa.

Since all of these are grazing animals, they have similar habits. Thus the place to look for them is on the grasslands. They will retire to heavy cover and brush-land for relief from the heat. They are for the most part gregarious and sometimes travel in very large herds. Herd animals are easy to follow because in addition to their tracks, much vegetation is trampled down by the passage of their heavy bodies. Being grazing animals, their food is soft and their dung is usually deposited in large shapeless masses. To get relief from insects, these animals frequently paw the dry earth and throw the dust up over their backs. They may create dry wallows where they take dust baths or wet wallows where they coat themselves with layers of mud. Some of these wallows may be twenty-five feet across and are easily seen. Frequently these animals will scratch themselves against a tree to relieve the itching of insect bites. This may eventually kill the tree if the animals persist and rub all the bark off. Chunks of their hair will often adhere to the rough bark and will help to identify the animal.

Although the cattle-like animals are heavy-bodied, the family *Bovidae* also encompasses the antelope-like animals which are among the most graceful of all creatures. From the large eland and topi of Africa to the black buck of India, the saiga of the Caucasus, the serow of China, the mountain goat and mountain sheep of North America and the gazelles of Asia and Africa, there are representatives of this group inhabiting every kind of terrain. They are found primarily on the grasslands but also in the swamps, deserts and on the highest mountain peaks according to the species. Thus their tracks may be found in mud, sand, dirt and snow. Although only the two main toenails will register under most conditions, the two "dewclaws" or small additional toenails

**(left)
Topis,** large antelope of Africa, measure over four feet at the shoulder and have sloping backs. Their faces are long and straight, with horns prominently ringed.

**(left)
The American **bison, often mistakenly called buffalo, were natives of the open plains. The present population numbers about 21,000 bison. They live in families but herd for migration.

up on either side of the back of the foot will show in deep mud or snow. The pronghorn antelope of the United States looks like these creatures, makes tracks like these creatures, yet belongs to a separate family because it is the only animal in the world that sheds its horns.

Tracking the Deer Family

THE FAMILY *Cervidae* contains the deer-like creatures. In this grouping it is only the males, with the exception of the caribou and reindeer, who grow antlers on their heads. In the *Bovidae* both the male and the female usually have horns. The difference between horns and

(top)
Antlers are important signs in tracking **elk**, for the animals cast them off once a year. But because the antlers provide food for other animals, they are often consumed before they can be found. Photographed at Grand Teton National Park, these elk with antlers still intact roam a snowy wildlife range.

(above, left)
Native to the arctic, the **musk ox** travels in large herds. In addition to their tracks, the **trampled underbrush** may serve as an indication of their passage.

(above, right)
In Africa, the **cape buffalo**, like other herd animals annoyed by insects, may paw up quantities of dust to throw over their backs. This **dust** and the **wallow holes** they leave in mud provide clues to their presence.

antlers is that horns, with the exception of the pronghorn, are not shed, but continue to grow throughout the life of the animal and are nourished by blood through their central core. Antlers are shed each year and receive their nourishment from a network of veins which grow on the outside of the antler in a soft velvet-like covering. The antlers stop growing in late summer and this "velvet" dries up and is scraped off. "Buck-rubs" are a not uncommon sight in the autumnal woods and are a sign eagerly sought by hunters. The males may score many trees in their area by rubbing their antlers up and down against them and by "shadow boxing" with saplings and small trees in preparation for the breeding season. The earth may be torn up around the base of such trees by the males' pawing or simply by the tremendous

TRACKS AND TRAILS / 249

(above) Now almost extinct, the American **bison** can still be found in small numbers on the plains and in captivity. Their tracks are large and similar to those made by the domestic cow.

(above) Clumps of hair attached to tree bark may help to trace an animal like this Mongolian **yak.** In scratching itself, the animal sometimes leaves this hair behind.

pressure they exert by their pushing, and the hoof marks will clearly show.

The cast antlers themselves are good signs to look for, as they offer positive identification of the animal. Many people are unaware that these animals actually shed their antlers because they have never found any lying about in the woods. If people cannot find the antlers, it is usually because other creatures have been there first. Antlers are composed mainly of calcium and phosphorous and since other animals need these elements in their diet, they chew the antlers. Rodents do this most frequently and any antler that lies out in the woods for any length of time will soon bear the sign of rodents' teeth. Clues as to which rodent made the gnawing marks can be found by measuring the width

(above, left) The only animal in the world to shed its horns, the **prong-horned antelope** is otherwise similar to the other antelopelike animals and leaves the same type of tracks.

(above, right) The African **eland** leaves **toenail** tracks. Massive in size, it has short legs and straight, spirally-twisted horns.

opposite page:
(top)
This **skull** of the **roe buck** shows its solid **antlers,** which are shed each year. Note that the canine teeth of the lower jaw are widely separated from the molars and incisors.

(center)
Found throughout the world in the spruce-fir forest belt, **moose** have long legs that enable them to move quickly through both forests and streams. Their tracks are large and show **dewclaws,** or extra toenails.

(bottom)
Many **deer,** such as this South American species, can sometimes be detected by the twigs they have chewed. Because deer have no top teeth in the front of their mouths, the twigs they bite off have jagged edges.

(far right)
During the summer months, the American **moose,** like this bull moose, photographed in Yellowstone Park, spend much of their time in lakes and rivers. Their long legs enable them to wade out for water lilies and other aquatic plants on which they feed. Young shoots and twigs of small trees also make up a major part of their diet.

of the tooth marks. Mice make the narrowest cuts, then squirrels, then rabbits, right up to the wide cuts made by the porcupines.

The moose, the largest members of the deer family, are found completely around the world in the taiga, the spruce-fir forest belt. The moose of Alaska and Canada are almost identical to those found in Scandinavia, Russia, Siberia and Manchuria, though in Eurasia they are not called moose. Their long legs allow them to trot swiftly through the forest, swim strongly through the lakes and streams and reach high for vegetation. Their tracks are found in mud, snow and sand.

Their methods of feeding leave a great many signs. Much of their time in summer is spent in the water where they feed upon aquatic plants; after they have eaten the leaves and the flowers off the lily plants, the stalks, relieved of this weight, jut up through the water. Moose frequently drop a lot of the water weeds and grasses which they feed upon and masses of these grasses float downstream and become caught on the brush. In feeding on willows, birches and other small trees, moose will frequently break the trees down with their body weight so that they can browse on the tops. It was the moose walking from one lake to another, by the easiest route, that established the portage trails in North America which have been used by Indians and their followers for centuries.

The red deer of Europe, the axis deer of India, Pere David's deer of China, the pampas deer of South America, and the elk, white-tailed and mule deer of North America are some of the better known members of this family. Their feeding habits vary. The red and white-tailed and mule deer are browsers and feed mainly upon brushy growth. Since deer do not have any teeth on top in the front of their mouths, the twigs they chew off have ragged edges. A rodent clipping off a twig, using its opposable incisors, will leave a neat, sharply cut tip. Some of the other deer graze upon grasses all the time.

Where too many deer are feeding in an area, they will completely defoliate the bushes and trees as high up as they can reach, leaving a definite "browse line" which can be seen for a long distance. In periods of extreme cold and deep snows, the northern deer will "yard" up by gathering together in a large group in some area where they can get protection from the weather. There they trample out paths or runways so that they can move about to search for food. Some "yards", after the browse has been consumed, become death traps. By the time the food is gone, the snow outside of the yard may be so deep that the weakened deer cannot leave the yard and will die of starvation.

In winter, when the diet is all browse, the dung of deer is dark, fairly dry and tightly compacted. In summer, when the deer feed upon softer vegetation and may graze, the dung is of a lighter hue, has more moisture and will be soft.

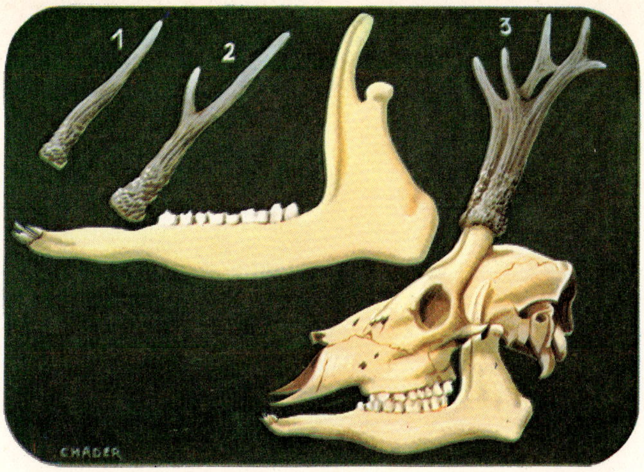
1
2
3
CHADER

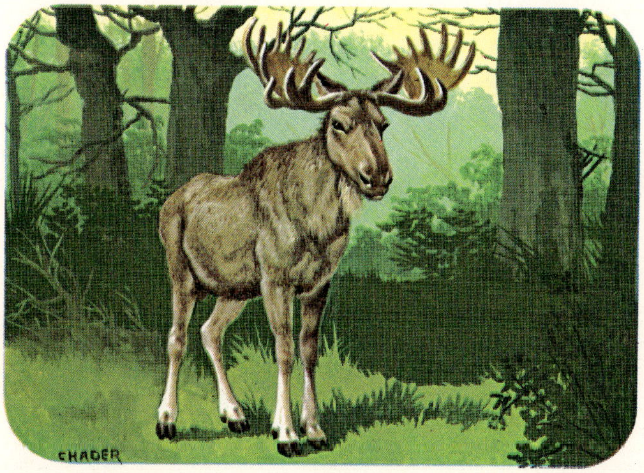
CHADER

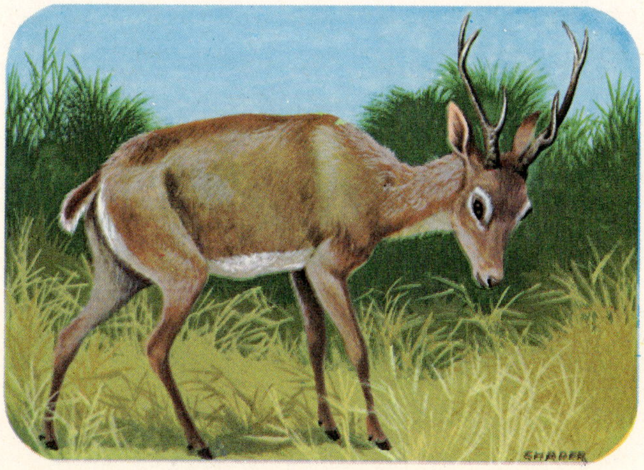

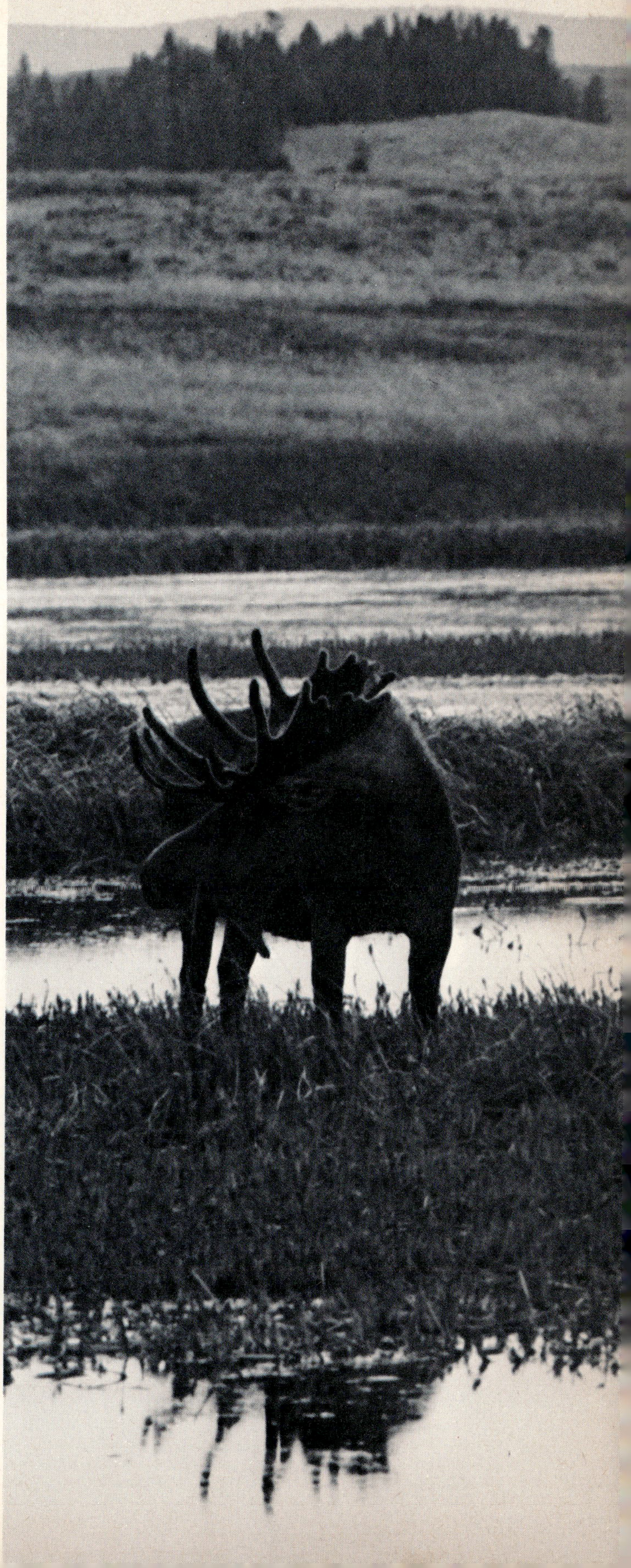

252 / ANIMAL WORLD

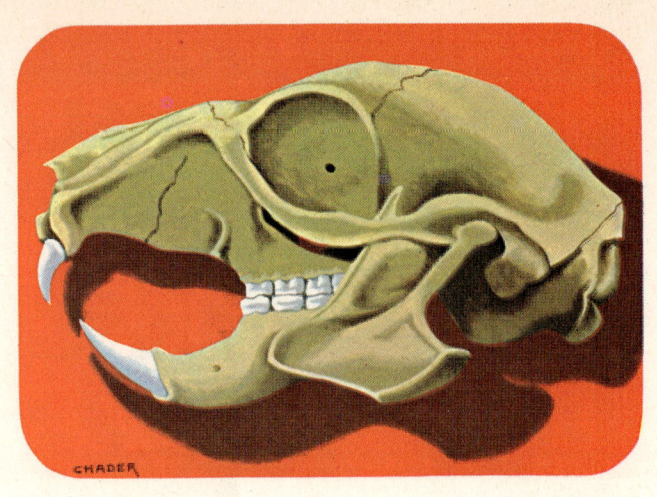

(above and top left)
The **peccary** is also called the "javelina" and sometimes the "musk hog." Peccaries have only three toes on their hind feet.

(top right)
Among rodents, **tooth marks** are important tracking signs. As pictured in the **squirrel skull** above, a rodent has one pair of incisor teeth in each jaw. These teeth grow constantly, and so the rodent must keep gnawing or cutting with them to prevent them from becoming too long.

Pigs, Domestic and Wild

THE TRACKS of domesticated pigs on the farm are identical to those of their forbears, the European wild hogs. The wart hogs of Africa and the peccaries of North, Central and South America are similar to European wild hogs. The constant rooting about and tearing up of the soil done by the wild pigs in their search for food leave enough sign so that their work is not likely to be confused with that of any of the other hoofed animals.

The Largest Rodent

THE RODENTS are the most numerous mammals in the world and as such are bound to be the ones with which man has the greatest contact. Although their tracks are important, their sign is even more so because it is more readily seen. Rodents are the creatures that dig things up, cut them down or gnaw them apart. They are the real construction experts and engineering geniuses of the animal world. Some of the other animal types may occasionally construct homes of their own but they really do not provide any competition for the rodents. All rodents have four incisor teeth in the front of their mouths which are constantly growing; therefore the rodents must keep gnawing or cutting with these teeth to prevent their becoming too long to be used.

The beaver is the largest rodent found in North America or Europe. More than any other animal, the beaver has the ability to change its surroundings to suit its own needs and in so doing leaves an extraordinary amount of sign. Because he is vulnerable to predation when upon dry land, a beaver must have deep water in order to survive. If there is not enough deep water in the area in which it wishes to live, the beaver will construct a dam to make the water deeper. The dam

TRACKS AND TRAILS / 253

Beaver cuttings (left) are made in preparation for a **dam** (below). Extraordinary engineering feats, these dams may be 1,000 feet long and contain many thousands of branches and bits of brush. Felled trees and cuttings are easily recognized as evidence of beaver activity in an area.

(above and right)
Beavers are easily identified by their **broad flat tails.** On each foot there are five toes, and the front feet are clawed for digging while the hind ones are webbed.

may be ten feet long or it may be 1,000 feet; it may be two feet high or twelve feet according to the terrain and its location. These dams rival those made by man and are often just as conspicuous. Even the smaller beaver dams contain thousands of pieces of brush and tree branches all

254 / ANIMAL WORLD

cut by the beaver, so that in addition to the dam, there is further evidence of beaver life in the hundreds of stumps which dot the surrounding area. Trees are felled for food, too, because the beaver feeds upon the bark, twigs and leaves. This kind of sign cannot be missed.

A beaver may build an elaborate house or it may live in a hole in the river bank. For years the European beaver was trapped almost to extinction. Because of this pressure, it abandoned the building of dams and lodges and lived only in river-bank holes. Now that almost complete protection has been provided for it, the dormant instinct has been re-activated and it again builds dams and lodges. A beaver lodge may measure as much as eight feet high and forty feet across. Even though

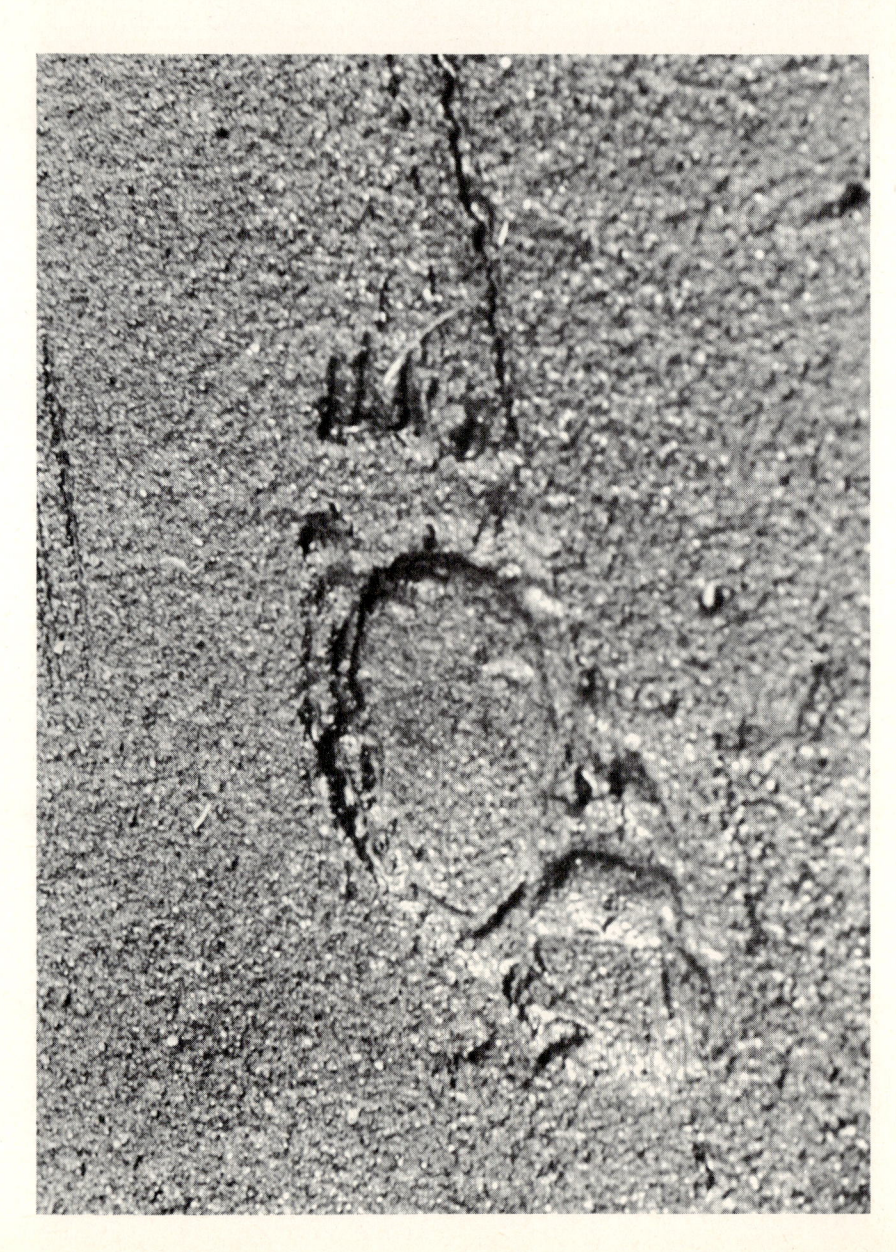

The **porcupine** has the largest, bare foot pad of any animal its size, and the toes point in for a **unique imprint.** The hind feet are specially adapted for climbing.

a beaver builds a lodge, it will also have three or four holes in the bank to be used as emergency dens. The beaver will also make escape tunnels by digging far back into the forest before surfacing. Then if the beaver is surprised in the forest while working, or if its enemy gets between the beaver and the water, the beaver will drop down into this tunnel and emerge to safety.

When all the food or building material has been used up in the area surrounding the beaver's pond, it will often dig canals to facilitate the floating of wood back to the pond. Some of these canals are hundreds of feet in length.

When a beaver cuts down a tree it turns its head sidewise to the tree and makes one bite high, then another bite low. Then, grasping the wood in between, a large chip is pulled loose. If a large tree is being felled some of the chips may be ten inches or more in length. The forest floor is soon littered with thousands of chips of bright wood. The beaver then pushes, pulls or drags the branches and logs to the water, creating broad, well-packed pathways in the process. As winter approaches, the beaver will pile a mass of branches under the water to be used for food when the pond's surface is sealed with ice. The tops of these branches stick out above the water and are very conspicuous.

Beaver tracks may be found in the mud bordering their pond. The beaver is one of the few rodents having five toes on each foot which show in the tracks. Since the front feet are not used in swimming, the long, strong toes are not webbed as are those on the huge back feet. The hind foot of a big beaver can be over six inches long and five inches wide across the webs. Beaver dung is seldom found because the beaver always voids in the water and there it rapidly soaks apart and decomposes. The beaver also makes piles of mud upon which it, and every passing beaver, will place castoreum, a glandular secretion with a penetrating scent, and more mud. These scent posts are easily located by both sight and smell.

Muskrats and Porcupines

THE MUSKRAT, which belongs to another family, also builds houses, but they are not so large nor so substantial as those of the beaver. Muskrat houses are constructed out of reeds, rushes or cattails, and may be five feet high. The area around the house is cleared of vegetation, which has been used in the construction of the house; thus the house and clearing show up very well in a dense swamp.

Some muskrats live in river and stream banks. Muskrats also dig small canals from one pot-hole to another, make well-used paths and deposit their dung on every prominent rock and log in their area. Their tracks may be found in the mud and there is no webbing between the widely spaced toes. The toes of the hind feet do have stiff bristles on them as an aid to swimming, which may show in the tracks. Five toes

Muskrat tracks are seen along the shores where they live and feed. The track usually shows a set of closely placed prints of the front and rear feet.

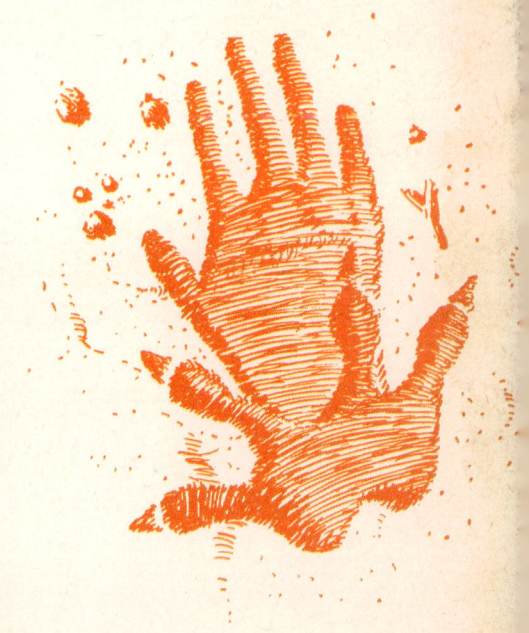

256 / ANIMAL WORLD

Similar to the European wild hogs, **peccaries** constantly root about for food, tearing up sod and grass as they go. The resulting disarray is a good clue to their presence.

Porcupines feed at dawn and dusk and also on moonlit nights. They will search out salt, gnawing on wood that has absorbed human sweat. Their quills, sometimes found at the entrance to their homes, together with their large tracks are the most definite signs that the animals are present.

show on both feet but the fifth toe on the front foot is rudimentary and small. Tail-drag marks usually show too. The muskrat has been introduced into Europe.

Porcupines are the largest rodents found in Africa. Members of this family also occur in Asia, Europe, and all the Americas. They are well known for their needle-sharp, barbed quills which are their main means of defending themselves. The Old World porcupines are more terrestrial in their habits and frequently dig deep tunnels or warrens. The New World porcupines also live in underground dens or rocky ledges and sometimes in hollow trees. Unlike their cousins, however, the New World porcupines spend most of their time climbing, resting and feeding in trees. They frequently do quite extensive damage to forests by girdling, which kills the trees. A porcupine may spend three or four weeks in a single tree and the ground beneath will be littered with pieces of bark and dark pellets of dung. Porcupines have an intense craving for salt; this adds to their conflict with man because they will chew anything that a man has touched with his sweaty hands. Axe, shovel, paddle and sledge-hammer handles impregnated with salt are a porcupine's delight and are avidly consumed.

The American porcupine has one of the largest foot-sole areas of all rodents of a similar size. The bare, elongated pad shows up well in the tracks and the fact that toenails register so far ahead of the pad proves that the nails are long and strong as befits a climbing animal. The tracks, scattered dung and dropped quills found at the entrances to their dens announce to all that here is the home of a porcupine.

CREDITS
Color photographs and illustrations appearing in this volume were supplied by the following: Photo Researchers, Inc.; The American Museum of Natural History; Armando Curcio; Doubleday & Company, Inc.; U.S. Department of the Interior, National Park Service; and H. S. Stuttman Co., Inc.

Cover illustration and illustration on pages 162-163 were photographed at The American Museum of Natural History.

Continued in Volume 3